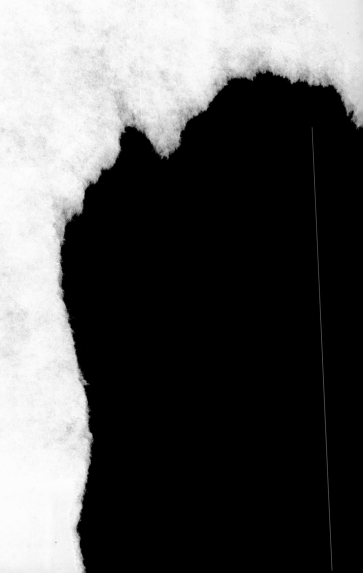

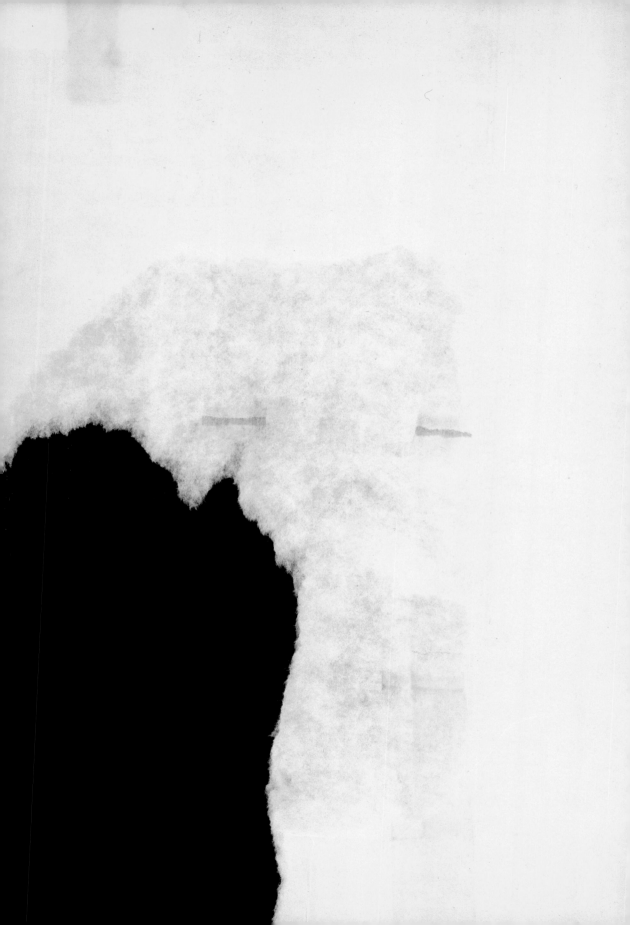

THE GRASSES

Earth's Green Wealth

ALMA CHESNUT MOORE

New York • THE MACMILLAN COMPANY • *1960*

First Printing

The Macmillan Company, New York
Brett-Macmillan Ltd., Galt, Ontario

Printed in the United States of America

Library of Congress catalog card number:
60–5085

In memory of

VICTOR KING CHESNUT

Acknowledgments

For the accuracy of these pages I am indebted to more than half a dozen outstanding American scientists. Dr. O. E. Jennings, Director Emeritus of the Carnegie Museum and a friend of newspaper days, painstakingly reviewed the first draft and made suggestions which I later followed. I was pleased that he liked the manuscript well enough to write a preface for me. Dr. Floyd A. McClure of the Smithsonian Institution and Harvard University, a specialist in tropical forestry and an authority on the bamboos, checked the chapter, "Giant Grass," and clarified the mystery of the "tear drop" bamboos. Dr. H. E. Glenn, Director of Planning, Clemson Agricultural College, sent me material on modern structural uses of bamboo.

Dr. L. F. Martin, sugarcane authority of the Agricultural Research Service, United States Department of Agriculture, reviewed the chapter titled "The Grass That Gives Us Sugar," and at his suggestion the chapter was read also by Dr. George P. Meade, a member of the United States National Committee on Sugar Analysis, an affiliate of the International Committee for Uniform Methods of Sugar Analysis.

Dr. L. R. Combs, Chief of the Program Services Branch, Information Division of the Soil Conservation Service, supplied me with material for the chapter, "Grasses to the Rescue," and checked the chapter for accuracy. Dr. D. B. Blakely, Chief Agronomist of the service, also reviewed the conservation material. R. G. Dahms, authority on cereal and forage insects, United States Department of Agriculture, contributed material on the new insecticides.

L. E. Childers, Chief of the Current Information Branch, United States Department of Agriculture, was most helpful in sending me pamphlets, bulletins, leaflets, and current news releases on all subjects covered in this book. From these and from the Department of Agriculture's yearbooks, I have borrowed freely and thus find myself indebted to countless men of science who, patiently and without fanfare, are working to improve American agriculture and to encourage wise use of the land. Finally—a confession that I sometimes felt at sea on so large a subject—I want to thank Jane Alva White for encouraging me to keep faith in my book and in my ability to present the story. Miss White retired recently from Carnegie Institute where, for twenty-five years, she served as Supervisor of Science in the Division of Education.

For permission to quote the last line of "Grass" by Carl Sandburg, thanks are due to Henry Holt and Company. For a brief selection from "Laughing Boy" by Oliver LaFarge, gratitude is expressed to Houghton Mifflin. And for two fragments from "Translations from the Chinese" by Arthur Waley, copyright 1919, 1941, by Alfred A. Knopf, Inc., appreciation goes to the publishing house of Knopf.

The Grasses: Earth's Green Wealth is in memory of my father, who led me when I was a very little child into the wonderland of science.

A. C. M.

Preface

The grass family consists of more than five thousand distinct kinds, out of a total of more than two hundred thousand kinds of plants which bear seeds. Were it not for the grasses, civilization as we know it today would not exist.

This book, *The Grasses,* by Alma Chesnut Moore, deals chiefly with grasses that produce the seeds, or grains, which are the basis of our starchy foods, our "daily bread," and which indirectly play an important part in the production of our meat and dairy products. It is interesting that out of more than two hundred thousand kinds of seed plants less than a dozen kinds furnish the main starchy foods of man. It is a frightening thought that if some plant disease or insect pest should somehow become so devastating as to practically destroy the crops of these few grasses, civilization as we now know it would suffer a staggering blow. Our country would be compelled to rely upon potatoes for the main starchy food, supplemented by buckwheat and beans, and the lack of corn alone would lead to great scarcity and high cost of meat, particularly pork and poultry.

The important breadstuffs of the world are derived from only about eight general kinds of grasses: wheat, corn, rice, barley, oats, rye, and the millets and sorghums. Limited amounts of wild rice are used, often as a luxury food, and here and there in various parts of the world various grass seeds have been eaten by native peoples, or are even today used in times of scarcity. The North American Indians ate the seeds of at least half a dozen grasses besides wild rice. We are told that in the Balkans even the seeds of our pestiferous crab grass are sometimes used for porridge. The seeds of the foxtail grasses (*Setaria*) are eaten in parts of Europe and some of the barnyard grasses (*Echinochloa*) were used as food by the North American Indians and southern Asiatics. The wonder of it is that not more of the grasses were developed by man through the ages to become important grain crops.

Stone Age man lived by hunting or fishing and by gathering edible plant products such as seeds, fruits, and roots. He sometimes had fairly permanent camp sites and around the refuse heaps lost or discarded seeds or roots must have grown, often more luxuriously than in their native habitat. From such circumstances may have arisen a primitive agriculture. As Mrs. Moore indicates, the ancestral plants from which our modern grains originated are not so definitely known. In many cases our modern grains are apparently of hybrid origin. In any case they are very old and man has had many millennia in which to devise methods of cultivation and to develop various and more efficient economic uses of them.

In Mrs. Moore's book on grass, each of the grains is discussed at length as to possible origin, methods of cultivation and use, botanical character-istics, and many very interesting facts which to most of us are new. Few of us, for instance, know of the anti-oxidant properties of oat flour. Mixed with peanut butter it slows oxidation and prevents so rapid a develop-ment of rancidity, and for the same reason it is now used in various ways. In my boyhood days in the country where winter wear included high boots and heavy socks, we filled our boots at night with warm dry oats to dry them out and to take away the perspiration odor. Whoever thought of that surely did not know of the anti-oxidant property of oats. In the olden days necessity was the mother of invention and it promoted experi-mentation, sometimes as fruitful as in our modern research laboratories. Mrs. Moore has brought together in convenient form, and from various unrelated fields of activity, a surprising amount of highly interesting matter about grains and grasses that is well worth knowing.

O. E. Jennings
Carnegie Museum
Pittsburgh, Pennsylvania

Contents

Beginnings and Dispersal

. . . let the earth bring forth grass . . .

Genesis I

When the waters of the earth were divided and dry land appeared, all life was in the sea and the earth was a desert of rocks and many-colored sands. Algae and other floating plants filled the waters, slowly building up silt and preparing the way for larger and more complicated forms.

Millions of years passed. Some of the plants from the sea learned to survive the ebb of the tides and live near the ocean's rim. Others moved inland after them, some growing to gigantic size. The coal forests with their club-moss "trees," giant horsetails, and tree ferns came and passed. Weird conifers, ancestors of our pines, and cycads, resembling palms but of a different family, grew and slowly changed as time wheeled by. The age of the dinosaurs dawned and had almost come to an end, when— somewhere, somehow—the first flower bloomed and the earth brought forth grass.

The first plants and trees on earth had no flowers and no seeds. They grew from microscopic dustlike particles called spores, as ferns, mosses, and many other plants still do. Their home was in watery bogs and shallow inland seas. But the grasses, when they came, could grow where the land was quite dry. They slowly spread a rich green mantle over the naked plains, conserving the thin new layer of soil against erosion by the wind and rain and encouraging the growth of other plants that we have today. As ages passed many varieties of grass developed, until there was a kind for every climate and amount of rain. By the time Stone Age man appeared there were real forests, and wide areas of the earth were covered with grasses of many kinds, rippling in the wind.

Some of the grasses had seeds that were good to eat. These came to be known as grains. Our word "grain" comes from the Latin word *granum*, meaning seed. When man discovered grains he was well on the road to civilization, ready to change his way of life from a wanderer to a

1

farmer who could stay in one place and establish a home. The supply of grain, without a doubt, brought previously untamed birds and animals to his door. These became the forerunners of the domestic animals and poultry we have today. The seeding grasses provided food for them too.

It is not difficult to imagine how man discovered that grains were good for food. Probably he saw birds and small animals eating them and decided to see what they were like. Soon he was harvesting the wild grains

and the women were making baskets and other containers to hold them. It was found that grains would keep for a long time, while other foods spoiled. Better and larger containers were needed. When a kind of earth was found that could be shaped and then hardened by fire, the art of pottery was born.

Seeds stored in a damp place developed sprouts and where grain had been spilled on the soft ground grasses came up the following spring. Some bright ancestor of ours put two and two together. The grass, he figured, comes from these seeds and if I put the seeds in the ground I shall have the good grass close by when I need it. Using a crude hoe or perhaps just a stick, he buried the seeds in the ground when the frost of winter had left it and thus grew the nourishing seeds near his home. We may be sure that it was not long before women found a way to grind the seeds between stones to make meal for bread.

The grains that we grow today do not differ so much from those grown in ancient times that we cannot recognize them, but, except for rice, the wild grasses from which they were developed cannot be identified with certainty now. They have either become extinct or been made unrecognizable by long cultivation. It can be assumed that the common-sense procedure of planting the largest and best seeds from each harvest occurred early to the first farmers of the world and that over a period of time new and improved varieties were produced which were very different from their wild ancestors. Selecting the best seeds from the best plants for next year's sowing is still practiced by farmers and plant scientists to improve the quality of our food crops and flowers.

We know beyond any doubt that cereal grasses were grown and their fruit used as food in many parts of the world and by different races of men at least eight thousand years ago and possibly as long ago as fifteen or twenty thousand years. Three varieties of barley and several kinds of wheat were found in the lake dwellings of Stone Age men in Switzerland and among relics of Bronze Age men in Italy. Grains of barley and wheat also were found in the tombs of ancient Egypt and Mesopotamia. Rice has been the staple food of the Far East from immemorial times, and in North and South America the prehistoric Incas, Mayas, and Aztecs built a complicated civilization upon the foundation of corn culture. Kernels of primitive corn estimated to be four thousand years old were found by scientists in a cave in central New Mexico. Small grains of a primitive variety were discovered in an ancient Peruvian tomb.

Agriculture, then, began with the cultivation of the grasses we call grains, or cereals; but grains represent only a few of the many varieties of grass that grow throughout the world. Estimates place the number of species as high as six thousand and botanists have classified more than five thousand species and many varieties. Grasses belong to the plant family *Gramineae,* the most important of all plant families to mankind.

Some grasses are so tender and soft—like the creeping bent on a lawn or golf course—that it is difficult to realize they belong to the same plant family as corn, growing more than twenty feet tall, sugarcane with its many-colored stems, or the giant among grasses, bamboo, which sometimes reaches a height of one hundred and twenty feet with a stem three feet in circumference. Sand and water grasses are of vast importance in the unending conflict between sea and land, though to many they are completely unknown. Others can reclaim wastelands, building and conserving soil and helping to regulate the flow of water and its storage in the earth. Grasses furnish products for healing, timber, paper, chemicals, and cloth. They cover our lawns and playing fields, and they are our main source of food. For in addition to the cereal grasses whose fruit nourishes both people and animals we must consider those used for grazing, silage, and hay.

In a rather special group are grasses that seem intended only to delight the senses. Some are so fragrant that their oils are distilled to make perfumes, such as the sweet-scented *Cymbopogon (Andropogon) schoenanthus,* sometimes called Indian grass or lemon grass. It grows wild extensively in India but it is also cultivated there and is found in some greenhouses of the West. An infusion made from its leaves is used as a tea in India and is believed to have a tonic effect. A fragrant oil distilled from the leaves is valued as a perfume. For this use it is raised in large quantities in Ceylon and other countries, for export. The scent is similar to that of verbena and it often passes under this name. Sometimes it is confused with citronella, a related fragrant grass.

Citronella oil is obtained from *Andropogon nardus,* cultivated in Ceylon and Singapore. In India it is valued highly as a remedy for rheumatism; in Europe and America it is used in soaps and perfumes.

Holy grass is *Savastana odorata.* In parts of northern Europe it is spread before the doors of churches and in the path of religious processions during festivals. Sometimes it is called vanilla grass, seneca grass, or sweet grass. There are eight or more species of this genus, distributed throughout northern Europe and North America. A large-leafed vanilla grass, *S. macrophylla,* is found in California. In the St. Lawrence River region of eastern Canada there is a slender variety, used by the Indians for dainty thin-walled baskets which keep indefinitely their sweet scent of new-mown hay. Another genus of sweet grass, *Panicularia,* owes its name to the fact that cattle are especially fond of the variety *P. fluitans.* Fragrant, too, is the miniature spring grass, *Anthoxanthum odoratum,* with its flat leaves and narrow panicles. This plant was brought to

North America from Europe long ago and spread quickly to the fields and meadows of nearly every state, where it adds its sweet scent to hay.

Other grasses, including many bamboos, are grown as ornamentals to provide attractive contrast with plants that have large, showy blossoms. Though the flowers of the grasses are nearly always small and unobtrusive they are produced abundantly in very pleasing arrangements. The feathery plumes and graceful panicles of many species, rising on delicate swaying stems from a clump of bright green leaves, make a lovely display. The flowering heads of winter bent, *Agrostis hiemalis,* cloud bent, *A. nebulosa,* the quaking grasses, *Briza maxima, B. media,* and *B. minor,* and hare's tail, *Lagurus ovatus,* can be dried and used as winter bouquets, either alone or combined with other plants.

Among large grasses that contribute their special beauty to parks and large estates are Chinese silvergrass, *Miscanthus sinensis,* sometimes miscalled "eulalia"; pampas grass, *Cortaderia selloana,* and uva grass, *Gynerium sagittatum.* Smaller grasses suitable for border and background planting in gardens include the quaking grasses already mentioned, also *Pennisetum setaceum* from the West Indies; feathertop, *P. villosum;* weeping love grass, *Eragrostis curvula;* feather love grass, *E. amabilis,* and Japanese love grass, *E. tenella.* Nor should we overlook ribbon grass, *Phalaris arundinacea picta,* with its short broad blades striped green and silvery white. This grass, prized for borders in old-fashioned gardens, has many names—lady's ribbons, painted grass, French grass, and gardener's garters.

Another interesting grass which may be planted as a curious exotic is Job's tears, *Coix lacryma-jobi,* whose seeds, shaped like a fluid drop, give the plant its name. Job's tears is a native of India and tropical Africa which has been spread widely throughout the tropical zone. The hard seed capsules, gray to bluish white with a finish like porcelain, are about the size of peas and ready-made for stringing. They are used as beads, for rosaries, and ornamental objects; as a medicine by the Chinese; and as a staple food among some of the hill tribes of India. This grass is related to maize and sometimes grows six to eight feet high.

It would be impossible to imagine gardens, parks, and playing fields without their soft green carpets of fine-leaved perennial lawn grasses. Such dainty grasses, renewed throughout the growing season, we take pretty much for granted. Only the mosses of damp shaded woodlands provide a comparable springy covering for the earth. In establishing a lawn, great care in preparing and fertilizing the soil and in selecting and planting the seed pays high dividends in beauty.

Different grasses are adapted to lawns in various regions. In the United States, for cool humid areas, the Department of Agriculture recommends Kentucky bluegrass, red and Alta fescue, redtop, bentgrass, rye grass, and *Zoysia japonica.* In the warm humid region good grasses for planting are Bermuda, centipede grass, St. Augustine grass, carpetgrass, and the *Zoysia* species. For dry areas the native buffalo grasses of the western plains and the grama grasses are suitable where irrigation is not practiced, and crested wheatgrass is used on the northern Great Plains. Kentucky bluegrass and bentgrass will thrive in the cooler parts of irrigated sections of dry areas and Bermuda grass where the climate is cooler.

Some of the grasses that make our lawns came from faraway places. Bermuda grass, *Cynodon dactylon,* in spite of its name, is a native of southeastern Asia, probably India. It is celebrated in the ancient Vedas as the "Preserver of Nations" and "Shield of India." It thrives in heat and sunshine, and without it the herds of India would perish. No one knows how or when Bermuda grass was brought to the United States, but as early as 1807 it was considered an important grass in the southern states. A long-lived perennial, it spreads by means of runners, underground rootstocks, and seed. It survives the driest of seasons, and its runners can cross rocks six feet wide.

Centipede grass, *Eremochloa ophiuroides,* has an unusual story too. After Frank N. Meyer, plant explorer for the United States Department of Agriculture, lost his life in the Yangtze River after years of work in China, an unlabeled packet of seeds was found among his belongings. When the seeds were planted a strange grass sprouted, a low-growing perennial that, like Bermuda grass, spread mainly by long creeping runners. At each joint of the runners a double row of roots appeared. These suggested the legs of a giant centipede and gave the grass its name. The new grass soon demonstrated its ability to grow on the poorest soil. Today it provides a dense green cover on southern lawns and in erosion control areas from the coastal plains of North Carolina southward and west to the Pacific coast.

"Grass," said Senator John Ingalls nearly a century ago, "is the forgiveness of nature—her constant benediction." Though many kinds of grass at first glance might appear useless, we may be sure that most of them have important work to do. They work valiantly to cover the wastelands, appearing wherever the earth is laid bare. They spring up in the forest when an old tree dies and guard the site against erosion until seedlings of new trees start their growth. They quickly cover neglected gardens and fields, striving always to safeguard and nourish the topsoil—that thin layer needed for plant life. The close growing stems of the grasses cover

the surface, retarding wind erosion, and the branching matted roots, penetrating deep into the earth, bind the soil, slowing the evaporation of moisture and holding both earth and water when it rains.

In areas where forests have been destroyed, the grasses quickly take the land in charge to save the topsoil. Then tall weeds and brambles appear and, last of all, seedling trees to restore the lost forest. In areas where there is not enough moisture for trees, which need a great deal of water, abandoned fields remain in grass. Where moisture is insufficient for grass to root and grow, vast wastelands of the world's deserts stretch across one-fourth of its surface—ever growing larger.

The earth's surface was divided by nature into regions of water, forest, grassland, and desert, each in its proper place and delicately balanced against one another. From the earliest times men have quarreled and fought for the lush zones, the wandering herdsman raiding the settled farmer and the farmer constantly encroaching upon the grasslands of the cattle raiser. When the ruthless Genghis Khan with his Mongol horde destroyed the canals that made Mesopotamia a garden, then swept through Asia and halfway across Europe, one of his goals was to restore the land where towns and cities stood to an unbroken grassland for grazing.

In spite of the grasses' persistence in the most difficult circumstances, grasslands, like forests, can be destroyed by men and reduced to unproductive desert and wasteland. Flood, famine, and erosion follow their abuse. The dust of ancient cities, in deserts that once were rich farming areas, attests the destruction of the fertile soil that nourished and gave them being.

About one-fifth of the globe and one-half of our country was once in grass. The great rolling green seas of grass and the semiarid stretches that support little other plant life the world over are known by many names—prairies, savannahs, pampas, downs, the veldt, plains, and steppes. The most fertile grasslands are often called "bread baskets" because they grow cereals so well. The prairies of the United States and Canada, the pampas of Argentina, the grain belts of Australia and the Russian Ukraine are the world's most important bread baskets today. They produce most of the grains that enter the world's market except rice, growing the important cereals that represent nearly half of the world's agricultural output.

The most important cereal grasses cultivated today are wheat, corn, rice, oats, and barley. But also extremely vital to certain areas are rye, millet, and sorghum. All contain, with variations in the amount, the main food elements that are essential to human and animal nutrition. In our country we obtain from them almost one-third of the food we need for heat and energy, and in other lands the proportion is very much higher. If we consider the secondary products of the grasses—meat, poultry, butter, milk, cheese, and eggs—we find ourselves even deeper in debt.

All of the grains we grow today were grown by Stone Age men. We have worked with them and improved them, but modern man for all his science has not developed one new cereal grain. By far the most important of all the grains in world trade, the true Queen of Cereals, is wheat. It cannot be equaled for bread. In the United States, however, Indian corn, or maize, is the King of Crops.

Also of vast importance as a food, preservative, and flavor improver is the tall grass of the tropics, sugarcane, known since ancient times. And in the Far East, as well as in the Americas, there grows abundantly a grass of a thousand uses, the varied, always graceful bamboo. These are some of the grasses we shall examine more closely. But all grasses are wonderful and some of the little known species, modest and unassuming, perform remarkable and urgent chores.

two

What Is the Grass?

I guess it is a uniform hieroglyphic . . .
sprouting alike in broad zones and narrow
zones . . .

Walt Whitman

In an earlier day the word "grass" was used for any kind of herbage browsed by horses, cattle, and sheep. Today it has been narrowed in meaning to cover specifically the members of the plant family *Gramineae*.

Grasses may grow only an inch tall or reach a height of more than one hundred feet. They may have tiny, almost invisible flowers in Lilliputian plumes, or great masses of blossoms on spikes or panicles a foot or two long. They may be annuals, lasting only a year; perennials living for two or three years; or, if they are bamboos, they may survive for thirty or forty years and perhaps longer. Some grasses make their home in the water or along the margins of streams and seas; others manage to grow in dry hot desert sands and frigid polar wastes. Though they differ widely in size, appearance, and usefulness, all true grasses are fashioned on a common plan. If you were to start a collection of grasses—and you could easily find at least a dozen kinds along a country road in June—you would have to pass by a number of plants commonly called grass, such as blue-eyed grass with its dainty star. A glance at the stem and the leaves usually will tell you whether the plant you have found is a true grass.

True grasses have spear-shaped leaves, two-ranked and alternate on a jointed stem, a single leaf growing at each joint, or *node*. The leaves, always parallel veined, have two distinct parts, the sheath and the blade. The base of the leaf, beginning at the node, forms a sheath which surrounds the stem closely like a split tube. Sometimes, however, the edges of the sheath are joined. Occasionally the sheaths are dilated; in a species of *Potamochloa,* an East Indian water grass, the dilated sheaths serve as floats. The base of the blade extends from the top of the sheath at a sharp angle. The lining of the sheath usually projects a short distance

10

above the base of the blade in a delicate whitish frill called a *ligule* or little tongue. Some grasses have appendages, one on either side at the base of the blade. These are called *auricles*. Many grasses, when not in bloom or seeding, can be identified by the ligule, which is always the same in any given species. In large grasses it is sometimes an inch long;

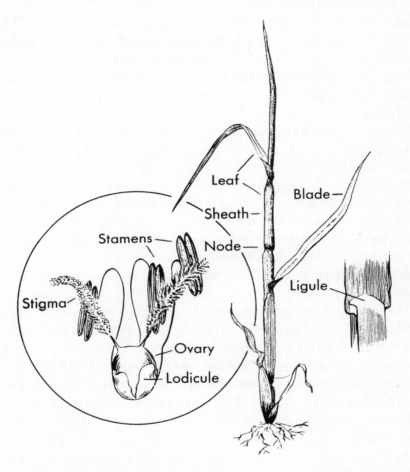

in others it is very small. Occasionally it is represented only by a hardened ring or fringe of hairs. This leaf structure of the grasses is unique and identifies the *Gramineae*.

Grasses send up from a single root many slender leaf-bearing stems called *culms*. The culms are erect, usually cylindrical and nearly always hollow except at the nodes, which are solid plates of tissue closing off each section. The sections of stem between the nodes are called *internodes*. In some grasses a few of the lower internodes may become enlarged and subglobular, forming storage space for plant foods; such grasses are termed "bulbous." The roots which send up multiple stems are themselves many branched, of great length, and equipped with millions of root hairs. The roots may penetrate the earth to a depth of five or more feet, forming a densely matted turf.

Efficiency is the outstanding characteristic of the grasses. There are no superfluous parts and each component has a function. The nodes are made of a very special kind of plant tissue which can swell and contract. If grass is bent down toward the earth, the nodes raise it again to its normal erect position. Cells on the side of the node near the earth elongate, forcing the stem up.

Growth of the stem continues for some time in the internodes, the increase taking place at the extreme base, just above the node. The sheath, which hugs the stem so closely in this area, strengthens and protects the tender growing section. The function of the ligule is to prevent rainwater, running down the blade, from entering the sheath. Chlorophyll in the leaves helps in the manufacture of sugar to nourish the growing plant, supplementing the mineral foods which the root hairs gather from the earth. The leaves also help regulate moisture. When water is scarce their edges often curl so that less surface is exposed and evaporation lessened.

The stems of grasses are smooth and highly polished. Their glossy finish, especially noticeable in the bamboos, is due to the preference of this plant family for the mineral element silica. In some of the bamboos a liquid accretion of silica is found in the joints. The silica strengthens and hardens the stem: when dried culms are burned it enables them to retain momentarily their skeletal form in the ash. Grass stems, or culms, as lawn keepers among us are unhappily aware, grow very rapidly. Some of the bamboos grow three or more feet in twenty-four hours.

As the distinctive leaf structure of the grasses identifies them as members of the family *Gramineae,* so the flower or seed head identifies the species. Flower heads differ widely in appearance, varying from the rough spiked bloom of corn and the bunched sumac-like head of some of the sorghums to the drooping panicles and dainty racemes of other species. The flowers of the grasses, protected by modified leaves, are usually tiny and arranged singly or in bunches on small flowering branches called *spikelets.* The axis of the spikelet, called a *rachilla,* is jointed like the culm and the flowers are two-ranked like the leaves. The spikelets in turn are arranged in various ways in the flowering head.

Grass flowers are usually perfect, that is, they bear both stamens and pistils, the male and female parts. Occasionally the stamens and pistils are in separate flowers, as in corn which produces male flowers in the tassel and female on a greatly thickened axis called the cob. Rarely, as in buffalo grass, may male and female flowers be borne on different plants.

In addition to the flowers themselves the spikelet bears two or more two-ranked modified leaves or *bracts*. The lowest two (one or both may be missing) are known as *glumes* and are empty. Flowering glumes are called *lemmas;* opposite and just above them is often a second bract called the *palea.* Sometimes the lemma has one or more long spiny projections at the tip which are known as *awns*. These bracts are modified leaves, which protect the flower and later the seed.

Grass flowers are pollinated by the wind or self-pollinated within closed blossoms. Thus they dispense with showy petals, bright colors, fragrance, and nectar which in other blooms attract the wandering butterfly and bee. The calyx and petals of gayer flowers are often represented in grass flowers by two or three tiny translucent scales, called *lodicules,* at their base. When flowering time is near, the lodicules are swollen with sap. They press the lemma and palea apart, opening the tiny bloom, and wither away.

Small and inconspicuous though they are, the flowers of the grasses are produced in great numbers and are not altogether colorless. The anthers of the stamens, lightly tilted at the tips of delicate filaments, are tinted delicately with spectrum colors—pale gold to orange and crimson, mauve to violet. Each breeze that shakes them sends pollen grains flying in vast numbers, for nature takes no chances with the fertilization of grass flowers. It has been estimated that a single anther of a rye flower contains about twenty thousand pollen grains.

Yet not all of the grasses bloom every year. The species that produce long underground stems often spread for miles by means of these alone and rarely have flowers. Bermuda grass, the cordgrasses, and centipede grass are examples. Although some of the bamboos bloom yearly, others flower at intervals of two to thirty-two years or more.

The fruit of all grasses is a *caryopsis,* or single-seeded fruit, wherein the seed coat, or *testa,* adheres closely to the fruit coat, or *pericarp.* These layers are difficult to separate. Though often very small, grass seeds are usually produced in lavish numbers and many are well equipped to travel. They can survive under varying conditions of soil and climate and grow in places where other plants die. Thus the grasses have the widest range of all the flowering plants and count in their ranks more individuals than any other plant family in the world.

Many grasses scatter their seed by dropping their short spikes all in one piece. If the axis of the flowering spike or raceme is jointed a single spikelet may fall with each joint. In spikelets with many flowers the jointed rachilla may break into as many pieces as there are seeds, each piece bearing a lemma, caryopsis, and palea. One-flowered spikelets often fall as a whole. The ripened panicles of still other grasses break off and are driven by the wind as tumbleweeds, scattering seed as they go. In polar regions, where the ripening of seed is uncertain, some arctic and alpine grasses have developed an ingenious method of reproducing. The entire spikelet, or perhaps a single flower, develops into a small-leafed shoot which drops to the ground and quickly takes root.

Very tiny seeds of many grasses travel the winds, a feat in which they are assisted by long silky hairs. High in the air they migrate to the world's far places to come to rest and grow. Outstanding among these high flyers are the seeds of Vasey grass, *Paspalum urvillei,* most of the beard-grasses, *Andropogon,* and those of the common reed, *Phragmites communis.* In Canary grass, *Phalaris,* the glumes have a membranous wing on the keel for wind gliding. Agnes Chase, grass expert of the Smithsonian Institution, says: "Some years ago entomologists exposed insect traps from an airplane to learn how high insects were carried by air currents. Numerous grass seeds found in the traps were given to me. The flat hairy spikelets of Vaseygrass were captured at a height of 4,000 feet. This grass was introduced from South America some sixty years ago [ca. 1900] and is now spontaneous from Virginia to southern California. Seeds, such as those of the common reed, the plumegrasses, most of the beardgrasses, and many others which are surrounded by long hairs, fly like thistle-down."

Some grasses also are distributed far by animals and men. These include the needlegrasses, *Stipa,* the three-awned grass, *Aristida,* and the sandbur, *Cenchrus.* The sharp-pointed bases of needlegrass seeds, the awns of the *Aristida,* and the barbed spines of the sandburs catch in the fur of animals, the plumage of birds, and the clothes of men and are carried to new locations. Awns are also used for burying seeds in the ground. In the

needlegrasses, some of the wild oats, and other species the glume forms
a sharp point which easily pierces the ground. Stiff upward-growing
hairs, above the point, discourage withdrawal of the seed. The awn is
bent; below the bend it is closely twisted. Sensitive to moisture, the awn
twists tight when it is dry and untwists when it is damp until the seed
is driven into the ground like a screw. When seeds such as this catch in
the fur of animals they may penetrate the skin and hurt them. Hitch-
hiking seeds of this type travel great distances.

As stowaways certain of the grasses have followed the world's trade
routes or arrived at new destinations as impurities in imported seeds.
Again we quote Mrs. Chase: "Grasses have spread over continents and
across the seas by the agency of man, often unintentionally. Guineagrass,
Bermuda grass, and molasses grass (in the tropics) are common wherever slaves were unloaded in the Americas. These African grasses, which
were used for bedding for slaves and as feed for such animals as were
carried, were unloaded with the slaves and ballast, and soon took pos-
session of suitable areas. Grasses spread along old trade routes and have
come in as impurities in imported seeds. Seeds of a strange millet were
found in 1932 by seed analysts in millet imported from China. It proved
to be *Setaria faberii,* an annual related to green foxtail. (Wild millets are
called foxtails or bristlegrasses in this country.) By 1947 it was found from
New York to North Carolina and west to Missouri and Nebraska."

Some of our most valued meadow grasses, such as Kentucky bluegrass,
spread so far and so fast in colonial days that they were considered
native, though they were really introductions from abroad.

Grass seeds vary in the length of time they live. Under hot humid
conditions they lose their ability to grow in one to three years. Seeds of

desert grasses, in their arid locations, may remain dormant in the sand for five or ten years, then spring to life when it rains. They grow while moisture remains in the sand, completing their tiny life cycle within a week; the seeds they leave, in their turn, wait patiently for rain. When seeds of the grasses are stored in a dry climate at relatively low temperatures, they may live as long as twenty-five years but ten years is usually the limit. Periodical reports that grain from the pyramids has been grown are simply not true. Good-*looking* grain is found repeatedly in such ancient locations but it is always without life.

Dr. W. E. Loomis, a botanist at Iowa State College who is specializing in seed storage, says that the life of grain and other seeds may be prolonged by low moisture, low temperature, and, with these conditions, low oxygen. He and his associates removed all moisture from corn and soybeans during their experiments and found that, even at complete dryness, seeds in air were killed by a temperature of 120 degrees Fahrenheit. This, he says, explains the failure to get *living* grain from the pyramids. Slow oxidation kills dry seeds. In contrast, Dr. Loomis found that seeds stored in nitrogen showed little injury. The experiment assumes that the dry seeds do not respire but start life again on the stored energy of phosphate bonds.

Grasses that produce edible seeds are called cereals, after Ceres, the Roman goddess of grain. They are winter or summer annuals, growing each year from seeds. Many other grasses are also annuals, but still others, such as the lawn grasses, are conveniently perennial. Grasses that spread by stolon and rhizome may cover acres of semiarid land, forming a thick network of roots to bind and hold the soil and a dense cover of leaf-bearing culms to prevent wind erosion. Protecting the land against erosion by wind and rain is one of the most important functions of the grasses. On rocky unproductive wastelands and dreary mudflats they can build land too.

three

Land Builders

I am the grass; I cover all.
Carl Sandburg

Riding the high winds, drifting on rivers and seas, carried by animals, birds, and men, seeds of the grasses travel to the world's far places in search of room to grow. Following vast and cyclic plans, each kind of grass finds its proper place—as trees, plants, and living creatures do— in nature's carefully balanced system. Because their needs are small, the grasses grow where other plants cannot flourish—on the lofty peaks of mountains, in the cracks and crannies of rocks, in polar regions, on watery flats, and on torrid desert sands. In these unpromising places, patiently over the years, they build new soil and extend their green dominion.

On crumbling expanses of loess and on soft rocks, weathered and broken by the wind and the rain or deposited by streams and glaciers, the grasses find an especially suitable home. Once they have gained a foothold, their roots probe downward in the mineral earth, seeking the modest food and water needs of their kind, binding the scanty soil in meshes of long delicate roots. As root and blade die and are renewed in their season, new soil is built, ever richer as the grass becomes more firmly entrenched. Fungi, bacteria, and microscopic animals appear to help in the soil building, attacking dead roots and releasing their organic and mineral foods for the growing grass. Root, blade, and dead organism thus combine to form the humus of good earth. As the humus deepens, increasing amounts of moisture can be held by the soil and more exacting and lush grasses can flourish.

To the developing grassland come insects and animals to burrow and prey upon one another for food. They too contribute to the soil building project, aerating the humus, mixing and stirring it, and contributing fresh organic and mineral substances. Slowly the soil deepens, more and more water is stored, and a richer vegetation develops. Along with it come higher

17

types of animals and plants. Thus was built much of our prairie land, covered and protected from the scouring winds by thick matted turf. Among the native prairie grasses, covering wide areas from the Canadian border down into central Mexico, is buffalo grass, which cures on the ground and provides year long grazing. So tough and deep is its sod that the pioneers used it to build houses and fences. Dust storms were unknown where the buffalo grass held sway.

Aquatic grasses protect shore lines and build land in watery places. They thrive where salt water washes their roots, and their tips are submerged by the tide. Their flowers open under the water, their pollen is water-borne, and their seeds are distributed by the waves. Such grasses are seed plants that developed on land but returned inexplicably to the sea, their remote ancestral home.

Many water grasses spread without dependence upon seeds. Their rhizomes creep through the silt of swamp and tidewater, weaving a network of fine matted roots to trap soil and vegetable matter, ever advancing their legions of green spears as they slowly build new land. Sometimes such grasses migrate in clumps and islands. When the dreaded *pororocca* —the rapid rising of the spring tide—sends a twelve- to fifteen-foot wave ripping down the mighty Amazon, the great beds of aquatic grass that line the river's verge are wrenched and torn away by the force of the flood. Large masses of grass drift downstream, seeking anchorage on new shores or in the arms of a quiet tributary. Here they take root and alter a shoreline. Similar islands of floating grasses form great barricades in the Nile.

"Our cordgrasses," writes Mrs. Chase, "have for ages been building meadowlands on mud flats and tidal estuaries in the Gulf of St. Lawrence, Chesapeake Bay, and the lesser inlets. These grasses thrive in the soft mud, submerged at high tide; their stout rhizomes form a firm network, ever pushing seaward on the shallows of the Continental Shelf. The coarse grass impedes the oncoming waves, causing the water to drop its silt; thus the grass protects the shore while building up the floor until it becomes marsh-meadow and, finally, dry land; at that time the cordgrass dies out and leaves the land ready for cultivation. Much of tidewater Virginia was built up by the cordgrasses.

"Smooth cordgrass, which ventures farther into the water than other species, extends its land building from Newfoundland to Texas. A few years ago when oysters were being transplanted from the Atlantic to the

Pacific coast, this grass was accidentally, but fortunately, introduced with them. By 1945 it formed a flourishing colony at Willapa Refuge in Pacific County, southwest Washington.

"A striking example of land building is going on today on a gigantic scale along the English Channel and the North Sea. The traveler on a ship entering Southampton today will see vast green meadows stretching into the sea. Two generations ago these were bare mud flats. *Spartina townsendii* (called ricegrass by the English), nearly related to our smooth cordgrass, was first observed on the Southampton salt marshes in 1870; it now occupies the tidal flats for 150 miles.

" 'These bottomless muds, though they stood empty of vegetation probably for thousands of years,' F. W. Oliver wrote, 'found no plant capable of solving the problems of invasion and establishment till *Spartina townsendii* came and made light of the task.' "

Mrs. Chase says it was one of the cordgrasses, *Spartina pectinata,* that converted vast stretches of marshland in the Middle West into rich black prairie. "But eons before that," she adds, "during the Miocene, when our Great Plains were being uplifted, the common reed must have stretched across the continent. Dr. A. P. Dachnowski, peat specialist for many years at the Department of Agriculture, found that the peat deposits throughout the Mississippi Valley and west to the Rockies are composed largely of the remains of this reed. Since this is a circumpolar species, it is probable that the flatlands of Finland, northern Russia, and Siberia were built up by this grass."

On the wind-whipped shores of lakes and oceans, where waves eternally assault the land, beachgrasses thrive and provide protection for inland farms by stilling the restless sands. Once firmly entrenched they build topsoil in which higher plants and even trees can grow. Beachgrasses belong to the genus *Ammophila,* a name derived from two Greek words, *ammos* meaning sand and *philos* loving. They are tough coarse perennials with stems about five feet tall, deep extensive root systems, and masses of tough basal leaves. Though they produce a spiky panicle of flowers nearly a foot long, the seeds which result are seldom fertile. The plants spread mainly by rhizomes. Beachgrasses grow very fast, often two feet or more in a season, and spread rapidly. They are the most important of all known plants for anchoring sand dunes which, unless opposed by vegetation, move inland a few feet each year, covering arable land and threatening buildings. Even young plants of this family stoutly withstand the cutting, wind-driven sand that moves eternally shoreward, up the windward side of the dune and over and down to the lee.

American beachgrass, *Ammophila breviligulata,* is found along the Atlantic coast from Newfoundland to North Carolina and on stretches of the Pacific shore. *Ammophila arenaria* is native to the north European coast but has also become established along both the Atlantic and Pacific shores of North America. The plants are very similar. As its scientific name suggests, the American species can be identified by the smaller size of its ligule.

The coarse stems of the beachgrasses form a mechanical barrier that protects the plants themselves from the scouring action of wind-driven sand. They force the wind to drop its sand, the thick clumps of leaves entangle it, and the roots bind and hold it. Beachgrasses push upward through sand no matter how deep the deposit becomes. They sprout new roots as they grow, while the stems multiply rapidly from underground buds to form large clumps and extensive root systems. Often stolons are produced too, which extend into bare areas and start new clumps growing. Decayed foliage and roots add organic matter to the developing soil. These grasses, established by nature along the shores of lakes and oceans, point the way to protecting valuable farmland against the creeping dune that seeks to bury and destroy it. They also provide a means of converting the dunes themselves to productive agricultural uses.

Sand dunes cover about 3,300,000,000 acres of the earth's surface, an area roughly twice the size of the United States, and for centuries men have sought a way to control them. Records show that as early as 1316 the problem was being studied in Germany. In Elizabethan England laws were enacted to protect the beachgrass on coastal sands. Colonists in New England, clinging precariously to the coast, also faced the problem of the dunes. Laws required the citizens of certain Massachusetts towns to plant beachgrass every year in April to safeguard shores and harbors.

Large dunes, unprotected by vegetation, can move many feet in a single storm. A succession of storms has been known to bury forests and villages under the sand. Sometimes, years afterward, winds blowing in the opposite direction have disinterred the ruins. Such storms are said to have assaulted the coast of Scotland in the winter of 1769, pounding an area where the beachgrasses had been uprooted. When the winds finally died down, only the tips of the tallest trees above the newly piled dunes showed where apple orchards had grown.

An authority on dunes, Professor H. T. U. Smith of the University of Massachusetts, says a preliminary computation he made several years ago indicates that dunes cover some 40,000 square miles in the United States, or about 1.4 per cent of the total land area. Many of the dunes, he adds, are covered with grass and were formed when the climate was more arid. The largest single area is in Nebraska which has about 20,000 square miles of dune terrain, used extensively for grazing. There are also large areas in other Great Plains states, but a relatively small area in the western deserts. Other dunes are located along the Atlantic and Pacific coasts, around the Great Lakes, and in nearly all of the inland states.

Dunes along the seashore and the margins of the Great Lakes are formed by coastwise currents that take sand from eroding headlands and from rivers where they enter the ocean and pile them at the water's edge. Winds, blowing inland, pile the sand in dunes. Inland dunes are formed by the wind in ancient lakebeds, along old beach lines and deltas, on the shores of rivers, and in desert and midgrass regions. Most of the inland dunes are rounded hills, clothed with native grasses and shrubs which have given them a thin layer of topsoil.

Scientists say that most of the active dunes in our country were caused by abuse of native vegetation—overgrazing by cattle and sheep and the failure to control blowouts while they were small. Other agents that may start sandy soil blowing are unusually heavy rains, serious droughts, fire, invasions by insects and rodents, construction work, and cultivation.

The only way to resolve the problem of the desert-producing dune is to reclothe it in protective vegetation. The mechanical barriers which are sometimes used are temporary measures—they cannot check permanently the slow steady drift of the sand.

Control of dunes at the mouth of the Columbia River in Oregon ended a serious threat to agricultural lands, homes, forts, military reservations, and ocean-going commerce worth millions of dollars. In the Middle West and Great Plains states dunes that threatened farms have been stopped. Converted to grasslands, large areas are now open to controlled grazing. In southeastern Colorado another control project restored thousands of acres of shifting dunes to vegetation and made unnecessary a project that would have rerouted a transcontinental railway across the Arkansas River.

Five steps are involved in stabilizing a sand dune. First, the incoming sand must be stopped at its source by establishing vegetation, mainly grasses, or by mechanical devices such as brush barricades, picket fences, or mulches. Second, the dune area must be returned to its original topography or to the topography of surrounding areas. Third, the initial sand-stilling cover must be established on the area where the dunes are active.

Fourth, the dune area must be seeded with additional perennial grasses which will assure the rapid development of permanent control. Last of all, the area must be managed with great care to maintain an adequate cover.

The ultimate goal of dune stabilization is a permanent covering of plants. What this will be is determined by the natural vegetation of the surrounding area—mixtures of the right grasses for the natural grasslands and of trees and shrubs for woodland zones.

Control of sand dunes opens them to use for limited grazing, recreation, wildlife protection, watershed cover, and woodlands. Dune stabilization is one facet of soil conservation as we practice it today. There are many others; in almost all, grasses play important roles. Of this we shall hear more later. We are now going to have a look at the grasses that supply our cereal grains.

Wheat, Queen of Cereals

(Triticum aestivum)

Back of the loaf is the snowy flour
And back of the flour the mill,
And back of the mill is the wheat and
the shower,
And the sun and the Father's will.

Maltbie Babcock

Wherever early man traveled, during fifteen to twenty thousand years of wandering over Europe and Asia, he carried with him for planting golden grains of wheat, the world's most important food.

No one can know for certain where wheat was first grown or by what people. The wild ancestor of our bread wheats has never been found among the grasses of the world and the varieties we grow today quickly die out if left untended. When history began, the growing of wheat was already ancient and its origin legendary.

Although the bread wheats originated at least five thousand years ago, the quest for their grass ancestors is unending. The long patient search is not designed merely to satisfy man's curiosity. Some closely related grasses have proved invaluable to the wheat breeder in crosses to produce better grain together with plants that can resist devastating stem rusts and other diseases that attack them. This search for wild wheats and attempts to classify the hundreds of varieties grown throughout the world today have yielded a fascinating conception of wheat evolution, which has been outlined by Paul Mangelsdorf.

When Nikolai Vavilov, the Russian geneticist and botanist, attempted to classify the wheats of the world, he studied more than 13,000 samples from every part of the globe. He recognized fourteen distinct species. Others make the tally slightly higher or lower, but experts agree that there are three main groups based on the number of chromosomes in their cells: seven, fourteen, or twenty-one.

24

The fourteen and twenty-one chromosome wheats are believed to have originated from seven-chromosome varieties and related wild grasses by natural hybridization followed by chromosome doubling. Such "cataclysmic evolution," says Mangelsdorf, is the only known method by which new true-breeding species can be created almost overnight.

Emmer (center) and spelt.

Einkorn (*Triticum monococcum*) and *T. aegilopoides,* sometimes called wild einkorn, both with seven chromosomes, are probably the most ancient of all wheats. They have impractically brittle stems, one grain in each spikelet, and tightly clinging hulls. Einkorn is believed to have originated in or near the mountains of northeastern Turkey. *T. aegilopoides* still grows wild in the hills of western Asia and southeastern Europe.

Einkorn, or possibly its wild relative, and a seven-chromosome grass (not identified but quite likely of the genus *Aegilops*) are believed to have hybridized to produce the fourteen-chromosome wheats. One of these, a kind of emmer (*Triticum dicoccoides*), grows wild today in parts of the Near East. Emmer itself (*T. dicoccum*) has been cultivated there and in adjacent regions of Africa and Asia since antiquity.

The cultivated fourteen-chromosome wheats were the first kinds to have tough stems and grains that thresh free. In addition to one which the Russians have recently discovered being grown in Georgia, there are four other species in this category. Of these, however, *Triticum durum,* macaroni wheat, is the only one of commercial importance. The Russian species, *T. timopheevi,* because of its disease resistance may become important in breeding new types of wheat for the future.

The twenty-one-chromosome wheats (three sets of seven chromosomes) are believed to be the products of accidental hybridization of fourteen-chromosome wheats with a wild seven-chromosome relative, almost certainly a grass of the genus *Aegilops* (possibly *A. squarrosa*). All twenty-one-chromosome wheats are cultivated and none has ever been found growing wild. These are our bread wheats. There are five species. *Triticum spelta* (spelt) and *T. macha* are hard-threshing wheats and they are not grown extensively. *T. aestivum* (common wheat), *T. compactum* (club wheat), and *T. sphaerococcum* (shot wheat) are the species grown today. They represent about ninety per cent of all wheat planted on an area of some four hundred million acres. All of these wheats are closely related and easily crossed.

The mystery of the hybridization that produced the bread wheats, remarkable for the quality of their gluten, remains unexplained. They may be the result of three hybridizations between fourteen-chromosome wheats and wild grass; they may represent three diverging lines of descent from a single hybridization; or they may have had a single unknown hybrid ancestor. Nor is it known where they first appeared or when. A cross between fourteen-chromosome Persian wheat and a wild grass that crosses with spelt has produced a wheat similar to common wheat and, since Persian wheat is known only in a limited part of northeastern Turkey and adjoining states of the Soviet Union, some authorities think common wheat originated there. Kernels of shot wheat have been found at Mohenjo-Daro in ruins dated to about 2500 B.C. Club wheat has been found in ancient Mesopotamian relics, and writings of the Chou period (about 1000 B.C.) describe a bread wheat in China resembling today's wheats with twenty-one chromosomes.

It may be that the ancestor of the bread wheats will never be identified —if it still exists—and that the land of its origin will never be ascertained beyond controversy. The nineteenth century Swiss botanist, A. P. de Candolle, after exhaustive research, concluded that the original home of wheat was Mesopotamia. He based his conclusions on philological data —a study of the names used for wheat in the oldest known languages— upon the observations of travelers, and the writings of ancient historians. Support for this theory is given by Berossus, the Chaldean historian, who said that wheat, sesame, palms, apples, and many kinds of shelled fruits grew wild in Babylonia.

Although most botanists feel that wheat was raised from a humble status to its present form by man's care, it is interesting to note briefly an opposite theory. Experiments in the cross breeding of various wheats and allied grasses produce an endless variety of forms, with fruits ranging from tiny seeds with closely adhering husks to large almost worthless kernels. Since a tendency to deviate widely from the norm is a characteristic of hybrid plants, the theory has been advanced that the wheat we grow today may be a degenerate form of a much nobler plant that flourished thousands of years ago. Herodotus, writing in the fifth century before Christ, said that the blade of the wheat plant and the barley plant in Mesopotamia "is often four fingers in breadth."

Long before history was written, wheat was being cultivated in Egypt, Mesopotamia, China, and Europe. Our earliest knowledge of wheat culture comes from evidence uncovered by the archaeologist's spade in the most ancient abodes of men. Lake dwellings of Stone Age men in Switzerland and of Bronze Age men in Italy have yielded several kinds of wheat and three varieties of barley. The magazine *Science* reported in November 1956 that radio-carbon datings for charred wheat from the dry bed of former Lake Wauwilersee, about thirty kilometers northwest of Lucerne, indicate an age of 4250 (plus or minus 200) B.C. This would make the wheat about 6,200 years old. In the debris of wattle villages along the Nile which date to Stone Age times, ancient granaries have been found. These were shallow pits dug in the earth and lined with straw. In one was a three-toothed sickle made of flint, its wooden handle still held firmly in place by an unknown glue. Other stone sickles of ancient origin were shaped like the new moon, similar to the ones still used today. Stone Age sites also have revealed saddle-shaped stones on which grain was ground with ball-shaped rocks. The presence among the relics of roasted grains reveals the ancient origin of parching.

The Egyptian story is continued later in pictures ornamenting temples and tombs. Friezes dated as far back as 4500 B.C. show men busily harvesting grain, donkeys threshing it, bags being filled and securely tied to be loaded on donkeys and taken to the granaries. These granaries appear to be man-high, truncated cones, perhaps of pottery.

In Mesopotamia wheat has been found that was put in storage thousands of years before Christ. Grains in a Sumerian jar, dated to 2500 B.C., were identified by several experts as *Triticum compactum,* a fine and highly developed species. Since *T. compactum* is a wheat vastly superior to spelt, the primitive wheat grown contemporaneously in Egypt, this would indicate that the Babylonians were ahead of the Egyptians in wheat culture. There is also evidence that they traded in wheat, sending it by caravan and ship to destinations on the plain and to countries fringing the wide desert expanses.

The discovery of Eridu in the desert of Iraq pushes the curtain back still farther in the land of the two rivers. Eridu was built on a site which was then at the tip of the Persian Gulf, by people who antedated even the Sumerians. The remains of eighteen cities were found, one above the other, and scientists date the first Eridu to possibly 5000 B.C. These people used copper implements, had a well-organized legal code, and grew cereal grains. In the debris of Eridu—and also at Susa—were found sickles made of earthenware.

When men began to record their activities and thoughts by means of stylized pictures and odd scripts such as cuneiform, they provided additional material for scholars to study. The old clay tablets of Mesopotamia reveal a lively trade in grain and other products. In the dust of long-dead cities were business files dating as far back as 3000 B.C. The files consisted of inscribed clay tablets carefully stowed away in jars. Included were shipping contracts, negotiations for loans, mortgage and rental agreements, records of real estate sales, and bills of lading for consignments to Ur, Uruk, and Nippur. The files reveal that by 2500 B.C. Mesopotamian merchants were forming trading companies, dealing in pottery and other wares, grains, wines, swords, and armor, which were being distributed as far as western Europe and the British Isles! From ancient records and relics we know that agriculture was flourishing in both Egypt and Babylonia four or five thousand years before Christ and that both wheat and barley were grown on irrigated land.

Up to about the ninth century before Christ, written history consisted of votive inscriptions on tombs and monuments, the records of kings, genealogies, dates of buildings, and business "papers." The Egyptians left no written history, and writing with a nail-shaped stylus on soft clay tablets did not encourage wordy accounts among the Babylonians. The first real narrative history we have is found in the books of the Old Testament, parts of which were written around 900 B.C.

In the story of Joseph in Egypt, whose experiences historians place in the Hyksos period—about 1700 B.C.—we have a record of the grain trade of long ago, of plenty and of famine, and of the importance of supplies stored against times of emergency. Joseph, the Hebrew slave, after he had interpreted Pharaoh's dream as a forecast of seven years of plenty followed by seven years of famine, was given the task of managing Egypt's wheat problem.

". . . in the seven plenteous years," says the Bible story, "the earth brought forth by handfuls. And he gathered up the food of the seven years . . . and laid up the food in the cities: the food of the field which was round about every city, laid he up the same. And Joseph gathered corn [grain] as the sand of the sea, very much, until he left numbering, for it was without number."

When the seven years were ended and the predicted famine came, Joseph found himself in a powerful and unique position. He had run, as one historian describes it, "the first and only successful corner in wheat."

When Joseph, "a man discreet and wise," stored large measures of wheat against the famine he anticipated, he was following on a vast scale a practice that was old even in Biblical times. In the dry climate of the desert countries wheat and barley could be stored safely for long periods without an appreciable loss of quality. One method of storage, in Egypt and in all oriental lands, was to put it into silo pits. In Turkey and Persia it was a practice of grain brokers to buy large supplies of wheat and barley when it was plentiful and cheap and store it for profitable sale during times of scarcity. In Malta, since ancient times, large amounts of wheat have been preserved in this way in hundreds of cylindrical pits cut into the limestone rock of the island. Some of the pits hold sixty to eighty tons. They are lined carefully with barley straw, filled with grain, and the small opening is sealed and then covered with a flat stone. From time to time samples are taken out and examined for signs of fermentation. If any hint of damage is found, the granaries are thoroughly cleaned and the wheat turned over. The silos, however, keep very dry and little trouble is experienced.

Many centuries after Joseph, Herodotus wrote his account of grain culture in Egypt and Mesopotamia in the fifth century B.C. and gave glimpses of a lively commerce in grains in the Mediterannean and Aegean regions. In the lush area of Egypt above Memphis, he said, agriculture was almost effortless because the flooding Nile did most of the work. The grain they live on, he emphasized, "is spelt, which some call zea." And again: "They live on bread made of spelt, which they form into loaves called *cyllestias*. Their drink is a wine which they obtain from barley as they have no vines in their country." With his reporter's eye for the picturesque, Herodotus adds, "Dough they knead with their feet." His account of agriculture in the Nile Delta continues:

". . . They obtain the fruits of the field with less trouble than any other people in the world, the rest of Egypt included, since they have no need to break up the ground with the plow, nor to use the hoe, nor to do any of the work which the rest of mankind finds necessary if they are to get a crop; but the husbandman waits till the river has of its own accord spread itself over the fields and withdrawn again to its bed, and then sows his plot of ground, and after sowing turns his swine into it (the swine tread in the grain) after which he has only to await the harvest. The swine serve him also to thresh the grain, which is then carried to the garner."

Herodotus also shed light on the methods used by Phoenician sailors to provision their ships on long voyages of discovery. A century or two earlier, Egypt's Pharaoh, Necos, had built a fleet of ships to explore the coast of Africa. He hired Phoenician sailors and ordered them to sail down the Red Sea (Persian Gulf and Indian Ocean) into the "southern sea," make for the Pillars of Hercules (Strait of Gibraltar) and return through them to Egypt by the Mediterranean Sea.

"When autumn came," wrote Herodotus, "they went ashore wherever they happened to be, and having sown a tract of land with corn [grain], waited until the grain was fit to cut. Having reaped it, they again set sail; and thus it came to pass that two whole years went by, and it was not till the third year that they doubled the Pillars of Hercules, and made good their voyage home." They had sailed completely around Africa, or Libya as it was called in that day.

Fruitful almost beyond belief was the Assyrio-Babylonian region, according to Herodotus. "But little rain falls in Assyria," he wrote, "enough however to make the grain begin to sprout, after which the plant is nourished and the ears formed by means of irrigation from the river. For the river does not, as in Egypt, overflow the corn-lands of its own accord, but is spread over them by the hand, or by the help of engines. The whole of Babylonia is, like Egypt, intersected with canals. The largest of them all, which runs towards the winter sun, and is impassable except in boats, is carried from the Euphrates into another stream, called the Tigris, the river upon which the town of Nineveh formerly stood. Of all the countries that we know there is none which is so fruitful in grain. It makes no pretension of growing the fig, the olive, the vine, or any other tree of the kind; but in grain it is so fruitful as to yield commonly two-hundred-fold, and when the production is greatest, even three-hundred-fold. . . . As for the millet and sesame, I shall not say to what height they grow, though within my own knowledge; for I am not ignorant that what I have already written concerning the fruitfulness of Babylonia must be incredible to those who have never visited the country."

Pliny, the Roman, later wrote that in Babylonia wheat was cut twice in a growing season, and afterward was still useful as pasturage for sheep.

The Greeks themselves had learned the art of sowing and reaping from the older Aegean race that occupied the peninsula when they invaded it around 2000 B.C. Several centuries later, during a period comparable to the Feudal Age in Europe, oppressed Greek farmers fled to Italy, Cyprus, Spain, and other parts of the Mediterranean region. Many settled in the rich farming area called the Pontus on the southern shore of the Black Sea. Here they sowed their wheat until the region was recognized as the granary of the world.

Herodotus tells how, during the Persian wars, King Xerxes at Abydos saw grain-laden ships passing through the Hellespont from the Euxine, bound for Aegina and the Peloponnese. His attendants, hearing that they were enemy vessels, looked to the Persian king to see if he would give a signal to capture them. But Xerxes asked:

"Whither are the ships bound?"

"For your foes, master," was the reply, "with grain aboard."

"We too are bound thither," replied Xerxes complacently. "What harm is it if they carry our provisions for us?"

In their conquests, which looked to the ultimate domination of Europe as well as Asia Minor, the Persians counted on seizing Greek and Scythian harvests to supply their vast army. This did not always work out satisfactorily. Herodotus tells of a forty-five-day retreat of the Persians toward the Hellespont, when all the grain that could be found or taken was so insufficient that "they gathered the grass that grew in the fields, and stripped the trees, whether wild or cultivated, of their bark and leaves and so fed themselves. They left nothing anywhere, so hard were they pressed by hunger."

In ancient Egypt, Rome, and Greece, so dominant was grain in the national economy that taxes often were paid in measures of it. Laws also were enacted to regulate the grain trade.

Although wheat culture was widespread throughout Europe during the Middle Ages, it was completely unknown in the Americas until Christopher Columbus took it to the West Indies in 1494. Humboldt mentions that it was introduced into Mexico accidentally in rice brought from Spain by a Negro slave belonging to Cortes. Humboldt further reported that at Quito, Peru, he had seen an earthen vase in which the first

wheat grown in South America had been brought from Ghent by a
Flemish monk. The English took wheat to Jamestown and their other
settlements, while the Dutch, Swedes, and other European pioneers
brought with them the favorite varieties of their homelands. Often, however, the early settlers preferred to grow Indian corn, or maize—a grain
entirely new to them—in preference to wheat.

What are the qualities that place wheat at the head of the list of all
the grains we know and use, and confer upon it the title, Queen of
Cereals? For food value, in comparison to its size, it has no equal in
nature. Its taste is mild and pleasing and it makes the best bread. Wheat
bread is light and fluffy because its food protein, gluten, has an elastic
quality not shared by other grains that enables it to hold in the tiny
gas bubbles produced when the action of yeast makes the bread rise.
Another reason for the high place wheat holds is that it is compact and
easy to store. Wheat can be kept in storage for many years without spoil-
ing if its moisture content is below thirteen per cent and it is stored under
conditions of low humidity. Thus it can be shipped easily around the
world.

Wheat also enjoys a wide climatic range. It is grown from the Equator
to the border of the Arctic Circle. It will thrive whether the rainfall is
scant or abundant. It flourishes at high or low altitudes—on low-lying
plains and more than ten thousand feet up on the high mountain plateaus
of Tibet, Mexico, Chile, and Abyssinia. A cool spring with normal rainfall and a summer that is hot and dry, especially during the time when
the grain is ripening, insure a good crop of wheat. Different varieties
are, of course, recommended for different regions and wheat has a preference for deep, well-drained loams and clay soils.

Wheat is a slender grass, two or more feet tall, which is related closely
to barley and rye. Its scientific name *Triticum* is derived from a Latin
word that means "to grind" or "to thresh." It is believed that the first
wheat planted had a single stalk, or straw, and a poorly developed head
that produced only a few small grains. So carefully has this plant been
tended, and over so long a period of time, that one seed planted today
can be expected to send up from five to fifty straws. Each head yields
from thirty to fifty grains, each plant three to four hundred. Wheat spikes
have a zigzag rachis with a single spikelet at each joint. A spikelet consists of several flowers or florets attached alternately to opposite sides of

a central axis or rachilla. Each spikelet is subtended by two broad glumes.
A floret consists of the lemma, caryopsis or grain, and the palea. In some
varieties the lemma has a slender spiny projection called an awn. Grains
with awns are classified as bearded, those without are said to be beardless,
or awnless.

As wheat was carried from one homeland to another by early wander-
ers and planted in varying climates through many centuries, it adjusted
slowly to new conditions of climate, rainfall, soil, and elevation. Many
varieties were produced. Later man took a hand, using his new scientific

knowledge to improve wheat. By patient experiments with imported
wheats, by selection, and by hybridization new strains are developed
constantly—plants that will give a higher yield of grain, resist diseases better, stand more cold, or more heat, varying amounts of moisture, and
different types of soil, or plants that produce a special kind of grain.
One variety succeeds another in the endless procession from the world's
agricultural experiment stations. Today, of about sixty-five varieties that
are grown in the eastern half of the United States, less than half a dozen
were even in existence one hundred years ago. Improved varieties are
developed by reserving wheat from the finest heads for seed, by crossing
different strains to bring out the best points of each, and by crossing
wheat plants with certain grasses. To cross the plants wheat breeders
put pollen from one flower on the flower of a different variety.

About two hundred and fifty varieties of wheat are grown in the
United States today. Over a period of ten years (1945–1954) an average

of 67,192,000 acres were planted in wheat and the annual yield averaged 1,148,289,000 bushels. As grain, five classes of wheat are recognized in commerce: hard red spring, soft red winter, hard red winter, durum, and white. Winter wheats are sown in the autumn in areas where they can survive the cold and are harvested the following summer. They get a better start than spring sown wheats, can be harvested earlier, and produce a higher yield. Hard red spring wheats are grown mainly in North and South Dakota, Minnesota, and Montana, where the winters are too cold for winter wheats. Hard red winter wheats are grown on more acres than any other kind. They are grown in two-thirds of the Great Plains states and in parts of Idaho, Washington, and Oregon. The leading producers are Kansas, Nebraska, Oklahoma, and Texas.

Most of the durum wheats are grown in North Dakota, though they can be grown in any region where the hard red spring wheats flourish. White wheats are sown in parts of New York, Michigan, California, and the Pacific Northwest.

The soft wheats, produced in areas of heavy rainfall, are high in starch content but low in gluten. They are excellent for pastries and make good bread when they are mixed with other flours. The hard wheats are rich in gluten and therefore make excellent bread. Durum wheats are especially hard. They are preferred by manufacturers of macaroni, spaghetti, vermicelli, and similar products.

Several very ancient wheats still being grown on a limited scale are einkorn, emmer, and spelt. Emmer, sometimes called amel-corn, is hardy and disease resistant. It will grow in very poor soil and in semiarid regions. Today it is being raised on small acreages in parts of Russia, Abyssinia, several European countries, and the United States. Spelt, sometimes called dinkel wheat, is very hardy and is still grown in cold mountainous areas of Europe and in parts of our own country. In the United States these primitive wheats are used principally to feed livestock. They are difficult to thresh and unsuitable for flour.

Wheat is easy to grow and farmers can select the varieties that are most suitable to their particular areas by consulting local farm bureaus. The seed may be sown broadcast but in the United States practically all of it is drilled in close, furrow, or semifurrow drills. Cultivation is not needed because the plants grow so close together that they choke out weeds. As harvest time approaches the farmer watches the wheat very carefully. For cutting with a combine it must be dead ripe because if the moisture

content of the grains is more than fourteen per cent it must be dried artificially before it can be stored safely.

We have come a long way since the old days, when wheat was planted
with a stick or a hoe, harvested with sickles or cradles, and threshed
by tramping animals or with flails. Such primitive methods are still used
in out-of-the-way corners of the world, but in the big grain-producing
areas of modern countries machinery does the planting, harvesting, and
threshing. The wheat, carefully graded, is stored in giant warehouses
called elevators, and sold through vast business organizations which send
it around the world.

So valuable is wheat as a human food that little of it finds its way
into other channels. When it is used for flour, the outer layers of the kernel
usually are stripped away and the germ, or growing part, also is removed.
The result is snowy flour, which is attractive to use but less nourishing
than graham flour, made by milling whole grains. Sometimes vitamins
are added to white flour to take the place of those lost with the bran
layers and germ. For use in our homes we can choose various types of
flour. If it is to be used for cake or pastries, it is best to select a brand sold
for this purpose because it is made from especially suitable kinds of
wheat. Bread flours should be chosen for yeast breads and rolls. Flour
companies employ specialists to study various aspects of flour and work
is continually in progress to improve the quality of different types by a
careful selection of wheat varieties and by skillful blends.

Aside from breads, cakes, cookies, and pastries, wheat finds its way to
the table in nourishing whole grain and creamy white cooked cereals,
and as wheat flakes, puffed wheat, shredded wheat, and bran flakes. In
England whole grains of hulled wheat are sometimes cooked in milk and
served with sugar and cinnamon in a dish called "frumenty."

Wheat starch is preferred by many laundries for use in finishing clothes
because it consists of both small and large granules. The small granules
work into the threads, while the larger ones remain on the surface of the
material to give it a smooth finish. Sometimes wheat and corn starch are
mixed for laundry use.

Another use for wheat is the making of paste for binding books and
hanging wallpaper. Monosodium glutamate, a flavor improver used like
salt, is made in part from wheat gluten. Plastics, fibers, films, and adhesives have also been produced from wheat gluten, but not yet on a
commercial scale because they tend to be brittle.

Parts of the wheat kernel that are left over when flour is milled are not wasted. They are used today, as in times long past, as a supplementary food for cattle, sheep, horses, swine, and poultry.

Indeed, from the time wheat sprouts from the ground, it finds a use in today's living. Sometimes it is planted just for forage. Sometimes stock is allowed to graze in the wheat during its early growth and then turned out of the field so that the plants can finish growing and produce a crop of grain. Newly grown wheat shoots are very nourishing. They are sometimes cut and dried for use as a poultry feed, and in parts of the Near East they are served at the table.

And now we come to wheat straw, a vast potential of raw material. Wheat straw according to scientists is the most important of our agricultural by-products from the standpoint of availability and range of industrial use. Every year in the United States about 95,000,000 tons are produced—a staggering total to which might be added 5,000,000 tons of other cereal straws not used for farm purposes.

Some of the straw is used as livestock feed, animal bedding, compost, mulch for strawberries and other plants, and as fertilizer. As fertilizer wheat straw contains important chemicals—nitrogen, phosphate, and potash—in amounts estimated to be worth from $4.50 to $7.00 a ton, depending upon agricultural conditions. Left in the field to be plowed in as a fertilizer, it has a value ranging from $6.00 to $18.00 an acre, according to experts of the United States Department of Agriculture. In addition it contributes organic materials to the soil. Some wheat straw is used in making corrugated paper for shipping containers. These uses merely dent the annual harvest. Fully half of the straw is burned or otherwise wasted.

The straw that is wasted each year in the United States, if used for paper and other products, *could* take care of the entire needs of the nation for cellulose. Grain straws are one of the oldest paper materials known, dating to ancient China. They are used for paper in other modern countries and paper was made from them here until the early nineteenth century. We relegated them to the scrap heap when a method was found for pulping wood. Wood was easy to get, our forests were vast, and it seemed as if they would last forever. We burned the straw and used wood for paper.

Today it is obvious to all thinking persons that our forests cannot last indefinitely at their present rate of use. We know too that they have functions more important than supplying cellulose that is obtainable from other sources. We use more paper than any other country in the world and, since World War II, consumption has doubled. The mills have been chewing up pulpwood faster than it can grow in spite of reforestation efforts; the supply is short, and costs are mounting. Scientific research has the answer to the problem in cereal straws which are renewed annually, in contrast to wood which takes years to grow. The technique of their use has been perfected by painstaking work and by pilot plant testing. It remains only for industry to take over.

Not only strawboard, but newsprint, high quality cardboards, and fine bleached papers can be made from cereal straws on a profitable basis. Research scientists have developed a mechanochemical process of pulping straw which makes use of practically the same equipment used for wood. In pilot plant tests it has been found that straw gives a higher yield of pulp than wood (fifty to fifty-two per cent of bleached pulp from wheat straw). The new method produces pulp in ten to twenty per cent of the time used for wood by the pressure method. Labor requirements, steam consumption, and total equipment costs are less. Safety hazards and insurance rates are lower. The pulp produced can be used for paper without the addition of other materials or can be blended with wood pulp when this is desired. Corrugated material, stiffer than that produced from wood, can now be made from straw, as well as high quality insulated building board, and boxboard strong enough to replace wood veneer in wirebound containers.

For the wheat farmer who today is eyeing his stacks of straw as potential raw materials rather than waste, government research scientists have proved that straw can be preserved in open storage by means of borax. Information also has been prepared on proper methods of baling straw and adaptation of one-man pickup balers to straw. By following the simple directions prepared by the Department of Agriculture, wheat farmers located near paper mills will obtain better straw, baled at lower cost, and stored without hazard, which can increase their income as use is made of this "waste" material for the production of fine paper products.

Full use of cereal straws and the culms of two giant grasses, which will be discussed in other chapters, would mean the saving of thousands of tons of wood, additional revenue for farmers, and lower production costs for industrial users of cellulose.

Thus wheat, perhaps man's earliest farm crop, retains today its age-old place as the world's most important food. As a plant it has been changed and improved beyond recognition from the wild grass that was planted thousands of years ago in the Stone Age gardens of Africa, Europe, and Asia. Modern agricultural science will undoubtedly continue

to improve it while technology seeks in laboratory and industrial plant new ways to use every part of the wonder grass, wheat. Because its uses are so vital, and because it makes the world's best bread, this grain above all others deserves the title Queen of Cereals. But hand in hand with wheat in making the world's bread goes a humbler, but very important and ancient, grain called barley.

five

Barley

(Hordeum sativum)

First I'll brew and then I'll bake . . .

From an old fairy tale

Writing nearly 2,000 years ago, the Roman naturalist Pliny said he believed barley was the most ancient cereal used by man. Pliny had made a wide survey of the books of his day, consulting hundreds of scrolls before writing his natural history. He may have been right.

Barley was grown in Egypt at the time of Moses and yeast produced by brewing it was used to leaven bread. A sacred book of the Chinese says that it was grown in China nearly 4,000 years ago. The Stone Age people of Switzerland used three varieties—two-rowed, six-rowed (large), and six-rowed (small)—grains of the different kinds being found in their lake dwellings. Men of the Bronze Age grew it in Italy. Barley was known to the Greeks and Romans and the small six-rowed variety, believed to be the most ancient of all, was the sacred barley of antiquity. Ceres is often shown with ears of barley plaited in her hair and they are also pictured on ancient Greek and Roman coins.

Another reason for believing that barley may have been known and used earlier than wheat is that it is the hardiest of all grains and has the widest range. It will flourish where other grains cannot be grown and does better in northern regions than any other cereal plant. Barley will grow in the Temperate Zone, as well as in Asia Minor, North Africa, India and other subtropical countries, and north to Finland, Norway, Iceland, and Alaska. It grows in Chile, Switzerland, and Abyssinia at elevations of 5,000 feet and in the high mountains of Tibet at levels 14,000 feet above the sea. This range is possible because there are many types of barley, adapted to a broad range of conditions. The greatest acreage, however, is found where the growing season is cool. Hot humid climates are not favorable, but sunny days during the ripening period insure high quality grain.

40

Two wild grasses found in West Asia (which *may* be what botanists
call "escapes" from some cultivated field) are very similar to barley
and are believed by some to be the ancestors of this ancient and still very
important member of the grain family. Wild two-rowed barley, *Hordeum
spontaneum,* is considered a possible ancestral form. Another is wild six-
rowed barley, *H. agriocrithon,* found in Tibet. This grass is still a vital
food crop in many countries such as India and Tibet, and in certain
parts of Europe where other grains do not grow well. In Japan it is second
to rice as a food staple.

The barley plant is a surface feeder. Its shallow fibrous roots develop
more quickly than those of wheat and the slim, usually hollow stems are
shorter. The leaves are wider than those of other grains and the sheath
at the base is much more prominent. Both head and grains resemble
wheat.

Some barley grains are hulled (covered), others hull-less (naked).
The hulled barley kernel is a floret with lemma and palea adhering to
the caryopsis or grain. Hull-less barley threshes free like ordinary wheat.
The lemma of the floret may be awned, hooded, or awnless. Most American barley is hulled and awned; hull-less barley is important in China
and Japan. Three species of cultivated barley are recognized: *Hordeum
vulgare* (six-rowed), *H. distichum* (two-rowed), and *H. irregulare* (not

grown commercially in the Western Hemisphere). Both spring and winter types are planted.

In the United States between twelve and thirteen million acres are devoted to barley. The leading states cultivating it are Minnesota, Wisconsin, South Dakota, Montana, and Iowa. The grain comes to our table in modest ways, is used for livestock, for making malt, and for industrial purposes.

Barley flour contains little or no gluten and will not make light porous bread, but barley bread and barley cakes are very nourishing and are still made in some parts of the world. Dehulled or "pearled" barley is used in cooking. Pearled barley, an ingredient of many soups, is made by grinding the grains into little balls. Patent barley is pearled barley ground fine to make nourishing soups and drinks and to modify milk for infants. Sprouted grains are used to make malt, which flavors some of our breakfast foods and soda-fountain drinks and goes into beer, ale, and whiskey. A by-product of malt is brewer's yeast, an ingredient of bread.

Before men knew about yeast they made bread in a very crude way. We can know almost exactly how they did it by studying the Stone Age implements that have been found. Using a curved or hollowed stone to hold the grain, they crushed wheat, barley, or millet with a ball-shaped rock. They mixed the meal with water and perhaps a little salt and baked it in the sun, over hot ashes, or on a flat hot stone. The bread was round and flat like a pancake and probably very hard. Samples have been found in Swiss lake dwellings. This was unleavened bread.

Leavened bread, made with the help of yeast produced from barley, is believed to have been made first in Egypt at least 5,000 years ago. For flour the ancient bakers used wheat, spelt, barley, and durra, a type of grain sorghum. The loaves were usually small and shaped somewhat like muffins, but long rolls were made—some sprinkled with little seeds like Vienna bread.

Brewing and baking, using barley and wheat, went hand in hand. Some believe that risen bread was not made until the art of brewing was discovered. Others think that the first leavened bread was produced accidentally when microscopic yeast plants (a kind of mold) settled from the air on a batch of uncovered dough and caused it to ferment. The careless cook baked the swollen mixture and got a real loaf of bread as we know it today. Of course it is impossible to know after so many centuries exactly how it happened. Fermentation is a natural process and its results were known long before the action was understood.

The Egyptians made beer by crushing slightly sprouted barley grains and mixing them with a little water to make a dough. They baked the dough lightly, then broke it up and made it into a mash again with water. To speed the brewing they added fermented mash. In this way they produced an alcoholic drink and the by-product, yeast, for bread-making. They did not know that they were making use of a plant so small as to be invisible to the naked eye, but they did know that something very astonishing happened to bread whenever they followed this ritual. We use barley today in much the same way.

In making barley malt the grain is cleaned carefully and soaked for about forty-eight hours in large steel tanks. The tanks are drained and the grain is kept in a moist fresh atmosphere for a week or more until it sprouts. It is then dried and the sprouts are removed. The result is malt and yeast. Malt contains two types of the tiny chemical dynamos know as enzymes which break down natural products to create something entirely different. Malt enzymes change starch to fermentable sugars. Not only is the starch in the malt itself altered, but also the starch in any grains that are mixed with the malt. This is why it is so useful in the brewing and distilling industries. Other grains can be malted, but barley does the best job.

Industrial alcohol also can be produced from barley. During the peak of World War II, when many important materials were in short supply, about 2,000,000 bushels of barley were diverted each month in the United States to make industrial alcohol for use in manufacturing artificial rubber and munitions.

Most of the barley raised in the United States now is used for feeding dairy and beef cattle, sheep, and pigs. The part of the grain that is removed when barley is pearled, the unfermented portions left when alcohols are made, and the sprouts that are removed during malting are all used in feed for animals. The yeast that is produced during brewing is not only packaged for use in baking but is a valuable source of the vitamins riboflavin and niacin, and similar products. Barley straw is used on farms as litter and for stock feeding.

Thus barley, perhaps the oldest grain man ever cultivated, continues its important role today. New uses have been found for it and, as science continues to expand its horizons, it probably will fill additional needs.

Corn, King of Crops

(Zea mays)

By red rocks the green corn grows,
Beautifully it grows . . .

From "Laughing Boy" by Oliver La Farge

A veil of deepest mystery surrounds the origin of corn, America's most important crop. Corn has never been found growing wild and no wild ancestor has been identified. It was unknown in Europe and Asia before America was discovered just as wheat was unknown in the New World. When corn is mentioned in the Bible and other ancient writings the word refers to all kinds of grain used for bread making. In England and Europe, "corn" is used specifically to designate the leading grain crop of any country. Wheat is England's corn, oats are often called the corn of Scotland, and ours is Indian corn, or maize. No mention or description of maize is found in early writings of the Old World and no relics have been found there.

So there is little doubt that corn originated in the Americas, probably in Mexico, and that it was a plant that the Indians took from the wilderness and developed beyond recognition along with other useful plants— including potatoes, tomatoes, green peppers, pumpkins, pineapples, peanuts, tobacco, and cocoa—which were unknown to Europeans.

Some believe that the Indians crossed a wild plant called *teosinte* with another grass to produce corn. Others think that *Tripsacum* or maybe podcorn, a kind of popcorn with individually husked kernels, may be its ancestor. But podcorn has never been found growing wild. Botanists are sure that corn is a hybrid because it has produced so many varieties. They can only guess where it was first grown and by what Indians. The newest theory is that teosinte, tripsacum, and corn are *all* descendants of a common ancestor that was lost in the dim period before history was written.

The Indian himself says either that he has always had corn, or explains its origin in beautiful legends of friendly creatures and miraculous be-

44

ings. In Rhode Island the Indians told Roger Williams that corn was brought to them by a crow from the Southwest and that therefore all crows must be protected. The Navajos said a turkey hen, flying from the direction of the morning star, brought them corn. In Ecuador the benefactors of the Cañari tribe were parrots. There had been a flood so terrible that only two brothers survived atop a high mountain. Two parrots came to their aid with food and a drink made from maize. When one of the birds was captured it became a beautiful woman who gave the brothers maize seed and taught them how to plant it and use it. She became the mother of the tribe.

The maize god Mondamin came to earth as a youth clad in bright green with waving plumes to bring corn to the Ojibways. And in the Great Lakes region the Great Spirit himself appeared as a beautiful woman, who instantly fell asleep. When she awoke and strolled through the land beans and pumpkins sprang up to right and left. Maize grew in her footsteps and tobacco where she had slept.

We may never solve the riddle of the origin of corn, but we can trace back through many centuries the story of corn culture in America. When agriculture was beginning in the Old World fifteen to twenty thousand years ago, Stone Age man was familiar with wheat and planted it wherever he migrated. In the New World, remote and unknown, the American Indian planted corn, laying an independent and firm foundation for the amazing civilization of the Mayas, Aztecs, and Incas.

It is generally believed that the Indian was a migrant from Asia who went across the ice of the Bering Sea toward the end of the last Ice Age. He came before wheat was known and has lived here for at least 20,000 years. Migrating southward, he reached the Mexican highlands around 15000 B.C. and, in a kinder climate, developed his agriculture and planted corn. He had no plow; his method was to clear little round patches of earth, make a hole in the center with a planting stick, and drop in the seeds. When he kicked the loose soil over the seeds the planting was finished. From this beginning grew the art, science, and religion of ancient America, and the architecture of fabulous lost cities rivaling Nineveh and Babylon. After about 5,000 years the Indian left the highlands of Mexico and moved eastward to a beautiful and fertile land on the coast of the Gulf of Mexico. Here he settled, calling himself *Maya,* "no trouble."

It cannot be proved, of course, that the Mayas were the first to plant corn because, far away in Peru, the Incas planted it too. But if the Mayas were the first, and even if they crossed wild grasses to produce it, remembrance of the origin of corn was lost long ago by this ancient race. A legend of the Mayas says that man himself was created from corn. The gods of creation, after destroying a worthless and irreverent race of wooden men in a great flood, created four men. "They made their flesh," runs the legend, "of the produce of the yellow and white cobs of maize,

and their legs and arms from the cobs themselves. These were our forefathers."

Whatever the origin of corn, its value was recognized quickly. It spread throughout the Indian's world and many varieties were developed, some for very special uses, for the Indian was a master plant breeder. He used corn as a green vegetable, parched ripe grains and ground them to make meal and flour. He made alcoholic drinks from corn and sometimes tinted them with red or purple seed coverings to give them an attractive color. He bred a sweet-stalked variety, said to have been as sweet as sugarcane, and probably made sirup from it. In tropical America he developed a giant corn whose stalks were hard and large enough to be used as a building material. Villages made of corn stalks are still found in Guatemala—the stalks fashioning walls, roofs, and fences.

Husks were shredded and used to stuff mattresses and cushions. Braided and twisted they were fashioned into mats, cordage, baskets, shoe soles, and dolls. They provided a covering for tamales, "paper" for small packages, and wrappings for cigarettes. Cobs were used as scrub brushes and hollowed to make bottles and jugs. Silks were believed to have a medicinal value. They were sometimes chopped and mixed with food, steeped in water to make a drink, or added to tobacco and smoked. Among the Navajos, corn pollen was added to soups and to special ritual breads.

Popcorn was a delicacy among the Indians from the immemorial past. Some grains of samples found in an Inca tomb about a thousand years old still popped. The Aztecs also used popcorn in religious rites. Temple virgins decked their heads with garlands of it for celebrations honoring the god of war and, in a fiesta for the gods of fishermen, it was scattered like flowers over the water.

We have hundreds of varieties of corn today but not a single important kind that was not known to the Indians when the first European settlers arrived in the New World. Then, as today, there were six main types: podcorn (grown as a curiosity), soft corn, sweet corn, popcorn, flint, and dent. Soft corn is used for flour and roasting ears. Sweet corn is the favorite for eating on the cob and has the least starch, while popcorn has the most. Flint and dent are used mainly as livestock feed.

Corn one foot high was grown in prehistoric America, as was corn twenty feet high, and varying sizes between. The Indians grew corn with one inch ears and corn with ears two feet long. They had corn with grains colored red, yellow, white, purple, and striped. In the Andean region of Bolivia, Peru, and Ecuador they liked large-grained soft corn. One variety had grains an inch long and almost an inch wide. The Indians planted their corn with prayers to the Great Spirit and to the gods of the corn, wind, and rain. They celebrated its harvest with a festival of thanksgiving. Indian artists modeled the corn plant in silver and gold, sculptured it in stone, made impressions of it with clay molds, and centered their religious rites upon the wonder of it. Fossil corn has never been found, but a clay model fooled the Smithsonian Institution for years. When it was finally dissected in the interest of science it was found to contain several pebbles and was pronounced to be a child's rattle.

While the mists of unremembered time obscure the means by which wheat and some of the other cereals reached Europe from their probable homelands in Asia, there is no mystery attending the arrival of corn in Europe. In 1492, when Columbus discovered Cuba, he found the Indians cultivating it. The size of the grains amazed him and he was very pleased with their taste. A year later, when he returned to Barcelona in triumph and bowed before the throne of his patrons, Ferdinand and Isabella, he presented them with an array of New World products. Among them were golden spikes of corn which, though little noted at the time, symbolized riches far greater than the sacks of gold pilfered from friendly Indians.

From Europe corn was taken to Africa by the Portuguese. In one generation it spread through Europe; in two, through Africa, India, Tibet, and China. Today it is grown wherever the climate will permit and often just for fodder in regions where there is not enough warmth and sunshine to ripen the ears.

For us, relative newcomers to America, the story of corn begins in the colonial days when the Indians befriended the struggling hungry settlers and gave them corn. Our method of growing and harvesting it is still based on what the Indians taught us more than three hundred years ago. They showed the colonists how to plant it in hills, with squash, beans, and pumpkins between the rows; how to use husking pins, and how to store the ripened ears in ventilated cribs. They demonstrated the use of lye in removing the hulls from the hard dry grains to make hominy and how to prepare and use cornmeal. Corn became the daily bread of the colonists. They planted it in preference to the wheat they had brought with them because it was easier to grow and use.

Over the years corn has lost none of its popularity in North America. On the basis of acreage planted and number of bushels harvested it is the most important crop in the United States today and the second most important in the world. The United States grows about half of the world's crop. Some 83,260,000 acres are planted in corn each year and the annual harvest is approximately 2,084,389,000 bushels. Of this staggering total, eighty or ninety per cent is stored by farmers and used to feed livestock.

And now for a closeup of this amazing New World plant that provides food for man in a bewildering array, grain and fodder for farm animals, and raw material for a hundred industrial uses. From tassel to root the corn plant is valuable. Even the cobs are used—and not just for pipes.

Tom Thumb popcorn, eighteen inches high with tiny ears, is probably the smallest corn grown today; some of the hybrids are as tall as twenty-eight feet. The long ribbony leaves at the joints of the stalks expose an enormous surface to the sun and are frilled and twisted so that they can swing and turn in the wind without being torn. At the tip of the stalk a spiked tassel develops as the plant grows. It contains male flowers. Farther down the stalk other spikes grow out from the leaf bases. These are the growing ears, snugly protected by many wrappings of special leaves and tipped with dainty pink or orchid silks. Each filament of silk

belongs to a female flower. Fertilized by pollen from the tassel, it will grow a grain of corn on the developing cob. When the flowers appear on the stalk, farmers say the corn is "tasseling out." When the soft hulls start to fill with a whitish liquid, they say it is "in the milk." After the milk stage has been reached the grains begin to harden.

We hear a great deal today about hybrid corns. A corn hybrid is made by crossing two types, or strains, of corn. The tassel of the plant to be crossed is removed before it develops, so that no pollen is produced. Pollen from the other plant is then dusted on the silk of the detasseled corn plant. Or the corn may be planted in a blocked field, isolated from other corn fields, with one row of the desired male parent planted between every two to four rows of female parent plants. The tassel then is removed from all the female parent plants so that the silks will receive pollen only from the desired male parents. The resulting seed corn often will combine the best qualities of the parent plants.

Hybrid corns are desirable because they give larger yields of improved quality and have a greater ability to resist damage from storms, disease, and other conditions. However, corn from a crop produced from hybrid seeds cannot be used for the following year's planting because the hybrids do not breed true. Farmers must buy new seeds each year if they favor hybrid corn. Some hybrids produce fifty or more bushels an acre, compared to the usual average of thirty, and have been known to yield as much as 200 bushels. But not all hybrids are valuable and state agricultural stations should be consulted for advice.

The widespread use of hybrid corns, which can be counted on for just a single crop, limits the supply of the kinds that are pollinated naturally, breed true, and are needed for seed to improve hybrid strains and develop new ones. To avoid the serious trouble that might develop from such a loss the United States Government maintains "corn banks" stocked with seeds of basic native varieties.

Most of the corn grown in the United States is produced in the section known as the "corn belt," which extends from western Ohio to eastern Nebraska. Iowa, Illinois, Minnesota, Indiana, Nebraska, and Ohio are the top-ranking corn states. Elsewhere corn is grown wherever the soil and climate are suitable.

Corn matures in a period varying from two to seven months. It is a heavy feeder, requiring fertile, well-drained, easily worked soil and a climate that provides adequate moisture, especially in hot weather. It needs plenty of sun when the plants are maturing, as well as security from frost and cold. Corn develops best when planted in rows in a well cultivated field with many neighbors to insure a good pollen supply. It is doubtful that it could survive, isolated, in a wild state. The field should be kept free of weeds and cultivation should be thorough but shallow, since the roots grow close to the surface. Because of its heavy food requirements, farmers often use a three-year rotation plan such as oats or barley, red clover, corn.

Corn deserves its world-wide popularity; no other grain has so many uses or can be presented as a food in such a variety of ways. No other plant has as many industrial uses, and the field is ever widening as chemurgy advances.

Because most of the corn raised in the United States stays on the farm to feed livestock, we should note first this important use. An ample supply of corn for beef cattle, cows, swine, chickens and other fowl goes a long way toward insuring a good meat supply. The green stalks may be cut and stored in silos to provide winter food for animals. Sometimes, after the ears have been gathered, farmers turn their cattle into the fields to feed on the stalks.

Corn comes to our tables on the cob in summer, as corn pudding, chowder, scalloped corn, fritters, and soup. Thanks to canning and freezing we can have it as a vegetable all the year around. We also have hominy and hominy grits, corn starch and corn flour for thickening soups and puddings, salad oil, corn sirup, and cereals such as corn pops, corn grits, corn flakes, and cornmeal mush. Corn crisps and corn snacks are somewhat new on the market. Cornmeal is used for spoon bread, a dozen varieties of cakes, breads, and pones, muffins, waffles, griddle cakes, and sausage stuffing.

To the Southwest and in Mexico, where Aztec cooking traditions linger, a special type of "big hominy" is ground very fine to produce *masa*. Masa is the basic ingredient of tamales, tortillas, hot cakes, cheese sticks, and cheese crisps.

Nor must we forget popcorn and the many confections made of it. During the last few years popcorn has become big business with the improvement of commercial popping methods and the spread of concessions at amusement parks and motion picture theaters. Electric home poppers have also given a boost to the industry. As a result the popcorn crop has been running between three and five million bushels a year, and hybrid varieties have improved the product. Today's popcorn is more "poppable." Have you ever wondered what makes it pop? Pressure built up by steam which is produced when the kernel is heated causes the Lilliputian explosions. The corn that pops best is the kind that contains a high concentration of hard starch; soft corns will not pop at all.

Popcorn plants are miniature, the corn having ears from one-and-a-half to six inches long and tiny hard kernels. The kernels may be of different colors, as those of other corns, and one variety has ears the color and shape of a very large strawberry. Another has thumb-sized golden ears.

The by-products of corn are almost endless and new uses are being discovered regularly. Before discussing some of the different materials found in the grain itself, let us see what can be done with the dried stalks, hulls, and cobs.

Cornstalks are used in barns as litter and for bedding cattle. They are also used as a filling in plastics and glue, for making insulating boards, strawboard, wood alcohol, and "Maizolith," a substitute for hard rubber. Mechanical pickers, however, have slowed their use in these fields because they break the stalks and make their collection uneconomical for large scale industrial purposes at this time, but the problem is being studied. The hulls and other parts of the grain that are left when cornmeal, hominy, starch, and glucose are made provide food for animals and poultry.

Corncobs have many uses, besides pipes. Ground, they are used as a sweeping compound, to clean furs, in mechanical tumblers to clean and polish metal articles and, with cornmeal, in many soaps—especially hand soaps—to increase their dirt-removing efficiency. Sometimes they are mixed with molasses and other food products to make an excellent kind of stock feed. Ground corncobs mixed with rice hulls are used with sandblast equipment to clean airplane and automobile engines, electric motors, generators, and other machinery. Paints, lacquers, and enamels not made of glass, can be removed efficiently from metals and other hard surfaces by this same method. Corncobs can be processed to produce a synthetic fuel and treated with chemicals to make alcohol, acetone, and butanol. Motor fuels have been produced from them experimentally and if necessary they could be used as a source of sugar.

Cooked under pressure with acids, corncobs produce furfural, an amber colored liquid that smells faintly like oil of bitter almonds. Furfural has many uses, the most important being the production of a compound called adiponitrile employed in making nylon. The second main use is the refining of Diesel, vegetable, and lubricating oils, and the third is the refining of butadiene for the production of synthetic rubber. Furfural is also used in the manufacture of plastics, to protect seeds from fungous growths, to preserve glue, remove paints and varnishes, dissolve plastics, heal athlete's foot, control slime deposits in water, and remove carbon from gasoline motors. In the medical field furfural derivatives are being used as antiseptics and research scientists are exploring their value as a supplement to such germ chasers as penicillin and streptomycin. They are also looking for substitutes for the important drugs, novocain and sulfanilimide. There are hundreds of furfural compounds and hundreds of uses for them. Furfural has many sources but aside from corncobs the other main commercial source is oat hulls.

And now we come back to the corn grains and ways in which they can be used in addition to their role as a food. A grain of corn, like any seed, consists of three main parts—the germ which contains the beginnings of the stem, the root, and the leaves of a new plant, a white filling called endosperm which nourishes the tiny plant, and the hull which protects it. Before corn is made into hominy or cornmeal the hulls are stripped away. The germ also is usually removed because it contains oils that quickly turn rancid. The germ parts supply salad and cooking oils, soap, glycerin, and sometimes nitroglycerin for dynamite. They can be treated with chemicals to produce "Pargol," a rubber substitute used for elastic sponges, rubberoid shoe soles, and erasers.

Cornstarch, made by milling whole grains, is used in cooking, as a substitute for talc in bath powders, and for starching clothes. Corn sirup, another product, goes on pancakes and into candies and milk formulas for babies. Gum for stamps and envelopes is also derived from cornstarch.

Gluten, a by-product of starch, is used in livestock feeds and in commercial resins, glues, and paints. A food seasoning, monosodium glutamate, can be derived from it. About half the content of gluten is protein of a very special kind that has seemingly endless commercial uses. It is called zein. Zein is an amazing chemical helper in many manufacturing processes and an ingredient of a score of products. It is seldom used alone. Zein is spun into a soft and durable textile fiber that is often blended with wool to produce worsteds and materials of unusual softness. It can be molded into hard resistant plastics and converted into a material like rubber. It is used in making beer and in improving flour. Zein goes into phonograph records, wave set for hair, chewing gum, varnishes, and printers' ink. It is one of the foaming agents used in fire extinguishers, an ingredient of linoleum and oil cloth, and a sizing for textiles. Zein will bind cork particles to form composition cork, and it will stiffen felt hats. It is used as an adhesive to bind paper, glass, wood veneer, and many materials that ordinary glue cannot handle.

In the paper industry zein also performs important functions. It is used for sizing, coating, and gluing paper and cardboard. A zein coating gives paper a glossy protective coating called overprint or label finish. Papers sized with zein resist oils, greases, waxes, and water and this makes them very useful for packaging and wrapping greasy foods.

Industrial alcohol can be made from corn. Bourbon whiskey owes its origin to the cornfields of Bourbon County, Kentucky.

Sugar from corn, called dextrose, is the kind that is found in human blood and corn sirup is especially digestible. In its turn, dextrose can be converted to sugar acids which are cheap to produce and mild to use. Their uses range from cleaning milk bottles and cans to the production of vitamins. From them also can be derived: a calcium salt used to treat milk fever in cows and to relieve bee stings; cream of tartar, used in making cakes and as an ingredient of baking powder; citric acid, also found in vinegar; citrate of magnesia, a medicine; ascorbic acid, which is the same as the vitamin C of oranges; lactic acid, a food acid which is widely used; and itaconic acid, for plastics and detergents. A great many more acids and acid derivatives could be listed which are of great importance in industry and medicine.

It would certainly be difficult to name a plant anywhere in the world more versatile than corn, the strange grass hybrid developed by the American Indians. No wonder it is that corn remains, as in centuries past, King of Crops in North America and that it has moved into second place on a world basis.

The Story of Rice

(Oryza sativa)

With morning rice at the temple
under the hill,
And evening wine at the island
in the lake . . .
Why should my thoughts turn to
my native land?

Po Chü-i (A.D. 815)

A student of oriental history tells us that in 2800 B.C., nearly 5,000 years ago, the Emperor Chin-nung of China ordained that the season of rice sowing would be opened by a special ceremony in which he himself would plant the first and best seeds. Seeds of four other kinds would then be sown by the princes of his family. From this account and from other ancient records it was long believed by many that rice culture began in China. This is not true, however. The many varieties of cultivated rice we have today came from a wild grass of India which the natives call *Newaree*, or *Nivara*. From India where it had been grown for thousands of years, rice spread eastward through China, Japan, Siam, and many islands of the Far East. The Arabs took it to Spain and from Spain it went all over Europe. It was unknown in North America when the colonists landed, though it had a wild cousin, and was not grown here until the end of the seventeenth century.

Beginning in 1647, Sir William Buckley tried for several years to grow rice in Virginia. His attempts ended in complete failure. This led to a general belief that rice would not grow in North America. But about fifty years later a vessel bound to Liverpool from Madagascar was blown far off course and her skipper put into Charleston, South Carolina, for repairs. Among those who boarded the ship was Landgrave Thomas Smith. Smith found that the cargo included rough (unhulled) rice and asked the captain to give him a small bag for seed. He had the rice

55

planted on swampy land and the result was a crop almost big enough to take care of the entire colony. By 1707 the project had become so successful that seventeen ships loaded with rice sailed from South Carolina for foreign ports. A system of water culture, introduced in 1784, resulted in a steady increase in the crop up to the time of the War Between the States. Later, rice growing was resumed and today some of the finest rice in the world is grown in the United States, with California, Texas, Louisiana, and Arkansas among the leading states which produce it.

Among cereal grains, rice stands next to wheat in importance as a human food crop and is pushing wheat closely on the basis of quantities produced. It provides the main food for about half of the human race.

The world crop has been estimated at about 200,000,000,000 pounds a year, about ninety-five percent of which is produced in Asia and nearby islands. Outside of Asia the principal rice producing countries are the United States, Italy, Spain, Egypt, Madagascar, and Brazil. Before World War II most of the rice in world trade was grown in Burma, Siam, and French Indochina.

Rice is an annual grass with long smooth narrow leaves and stems from two to five feet high. The spikelets with their flowers grow on a branched head which is erect at first but bends downward as the plant develops. Each spikelet bears a solitary flower. There are about two thousand varieties of rice, natural and hybrid, to suit many types of soil, climate, and methods of culture.

Rice thrives in warm humid regions of tropical and subtropical climates where fresh water is abundantly available, or on level land that has a tight soil or subsoil to prevent seepage and provide good surface drainage for irrigation. The plants *must* be submerged in from four to eight inches of water during most of their growing season. The only exception is upland rice, which is grown like other cereals and gives a lower yield.

In China and other countries of the Far East rice growing is a painstaking hand operation, the hoe being almost the only implement used. The seed rice is sown broadcast in a special seed bed, which is flooded with water when the plants reach a height of three inches. When they are six inches high the seed bed is drained and the little plants are taken up and carried into the swampy rice fields, where each one is planted by hand in the water-soaked earth. Water is kept in the fields until the plants are fifteen inches high. The fields are then drained, hand weeded, and hand cultivated with a hoe. This accomplished, the water is again turned into the field and flooding is continued until harvest time.

In parts of the orient, as the grain begins to ripen, a picturesque, centuries-old method is used to chase away the flocks of birds that descend upon the fields to share the harvest. This description comes from Dr. G. L. Hartwig's book, *The Tropical World,* and the setting is Java; similar accounts have come from Japan and other countries of the Far East.

"Cords to which scarecrows are attached traverse the field in every direction, and converge to a small watch-house, erected on high poles. Here the attentive villager sits, like a spider in the center of his web and, by pulling the cords, puts them from time to time in motion, whenever the wind is unwilling to undertake the office. Then the grotesque and noisy figures begin to rustle and to caper, and whole flocks of the neat little rice-bird or Java sparrow, *Loxia oryzivora,* rise on the wing and hurry off with all the haste of guilty fright."

Such methods are scarcely adaptable to the large-scale farming of North America. Essentially the same steps are followed—except that there is no transplanting from seed bed to field—but the work is done almost entirely with machines. The land is plowed, disked, harrowed, and leveled by motorized equipment and even the levees dividing the field into "cuts" are built by machines. The levees are to take care of small differences in the elevation of the land so that when the fields are flooded the water can be kept at a uniform level.

Water for irrigating the rice fields is sometimes obtained from streams and sometimes from wells. It is pumped from these sources and distributed to the fields by means of canals. Fairly level land with a gentle slope toward the drainage channels provides an ideal location for rice. When a new area is being opened for rice, the first step usually is the hiring of a surveyor to plan the location of the canals, drainage ditches, and levees.

For rice planting the land is plowed four to six inches deep, either in the spring or in the fall, disked, and then harrowed to provide a firm mellow surface for sowing. The seed is usually sown with grain drills set carefully for the proper depth, though often it is broadcast by planting machines or even by airplanes. Airplane seeding makes it possible to sow the seeds right in the water and in this case the rough rice is soaked in water before planting so that it will sprout quickly and not rot. Sometimes the water is kept on the fields after seeding in this manner; sometimes the fields are drained shortly after seeding and then resubmerged when the plants are well started. Water seeded rice tends to mature more evenly and to be freer of grass and weeds than rice sown in the ordinary way.

Airplane seeding in water is practiced almost invariably in California to control the many pestiferous weeds that invade the fields. The worst of these is barnyard grass or water grass, *Echinochloa crusgalli*. The rice is sown on water two to four inches deep and this level is maintained until seeding is completed. The level is then raised to four to eight inches and kept there until the crop is ready to harvest. If the seeds *are* sown in the soil, the fields are submerged immediately to a depth of four to eight inches, a level maintained until the grain is almost ripe.

Weeds do not present so serious a problem in the southern states. Although airplane seeding may be practiced, the rice is more often sown in the soil. When the plants are four to six inches high the land is flooded with one to two inches of water. The depth is increased gradually as the plants grow taller until it is four to eight inches deep in the fields. Then for the rest of the growing season it is kept at a depth of about five inches. When the rice is fully headed, with the panicles turned down and the grains in the upper parts nearly ripe, the land is drained. The rice continues to ripen and is ready for harvest in about two weeks.

Rice is harvested with combines or with rice binders. Combines may be either self-propelled or drawn by tractors—often both types are used together. They cut swaths from six to fourteen feet wide and thresh the grain as they go. When rice is harvested with combines it has to be dried artificially before it can be processed. When cut with a binder it is dried in the field in shocks and threshed later.

Rice grains when they leave the thresher are enclosed in husks and are known as rough rice, or paddy rice. In this state they can be set aside for seed or fed to livestock. For use on the table they are milled to remove the outer layers of the grain. When just the husk is removed we have brown rice, more nourishing than polished rice because it retains the valuable minerals, proteins, and vitamins contained in the outer layers of the kernel. Brown rice, however, is less attractive in appearance, harder to digest, and tends to spoil more quickly. Usually the bran layer is rubbed off at the mill and with it goes the germ, or growing part, and another lighter colored layer known as *polish*.

Milling rice requires great skill because, of all the grains, rice is the one most often used whole. Broken grains are not desirable in commercial packages. Yet, because rice is very brittle, nearly one-third are broken during milling and have to be sold at a lower price.

Rice stripped of its outer coverings by machinery, without pretreatment, loses nearly all of its oil, a great deal of its protein, and almost all of its minerals and vitamins. It is from ninety to ninety-four per cent pure starch. A diet composed almost exclusively of such rice produces a disease called beri-beri (weakness), a multiple neuritis due to lack of vitamin B. As early as 1890, Dr. Charles Hose, in Sarawak, suspected a dietary origin of this terrible disease. He noticed that it developed among natives employed on plantations, who were away from home for months at a time and fed on imported rice, and that their womenfolk at home, using freshly husked rice, were not affected. But years passed before the trouble was traced. Today beri-beri does not appear when rice is milled to preserve the bran layers and germ, or when vitamin B is added to polished rice.

Asiatics, whose practices we have been studying during recent years, store rough rice just as it comes from the thresher and mill it as it is needed; then, instead of using automatic machinery, they employ a mortar and pestle or a machine operated by hand. By this method the bran layer and germ are left on the rice and it is much more nourishing. Where such rice is the mainstay of the diet, beri-beri does not develop. Another practice which has been followed for years in India, Burma, the Malay Peninsula, and British Guiana—though not especially in China—is that of parboiling the rice before milling it. Soaking the rough rice, another oriental practice, makes removal of the hulls easier and, again, the rice is more nourishing. Equally clever are oriental methods of cooking rice.

The Western World has experimented with Asiatic methods of handling and cooking rice with good results; the trick of parboiling rice before milling it has been widely adopted. The method of preparing it may vary, but the general practice today is to soak the rough rice first in warm or hot water. After the water is drained off, the rice is steamed, carefully dried, then hulled and milled in the usual way. Scientists found that the parboiled rice, after being milled, still contained the important minerals and vitamins that ordinarily were lost. Instead of being discarded with the bran they had been absorbed by the grain. Most of the oil was still lost but this was just as well since rice oil spoils quickly. An added boon was that fewer grains were broken during milling, the cooking quality was improved, and the rice was more resistant to insects and spoilage. Parboiled rice is much easier to cook at home because it does not require rinsing or prolonged boiling, nor does it get sticky or go to pieces in soups. This new kind of rice is now sold widely in grocery stores.

While the East depends mainly upon rice and the West mainly on wheat as a basic food, we use a great deal of rice in our homes. We like to serve it with chicken, ham, or fish instead of potatoes and it is an important breakfast cereal appearing in many forms. Puffed rice is made by steaming the grains in a special type of bomb under heavy pressure. When the end of the bomb is opened suddenly at the proper instant, release of the pressure causes the grains to shoot out, greatly expanded in size. Puffed rice was first made more than fifty years ago. For rice flakes the rice is cooked, mixed with sirup and other flavoring materials, rolled thin, and then toasted in giant ovens. Sometimes the rice is popped in ovens with sugar, malt flavorings, vitamins, and iron added. Cream of rice is a granulated rice cereal, cooked like cream of wheat. Rice flour also is made.

For use as a vegetable we have a choice of brown rice, white rice, peeled rice which retains part of the bran, precooked rice, and even canned and frozen rice. New on the market are two kinds of snacks, both perfected by scientists doubling as chefs at laboratories maintained by the United States Department of Agriculture. Rice curls are made from whole or broken grains of rice. The rice is ground coarse and mixed to a paste with boiling water. Strings of the paste are then fried for about three minutes in hot oil to emerge crisp and golden brown. They are delicious flavored with salt and a little sodium glutamate. Sometimes they are made tangy with cheese, onion, celery, garlic, or smoked salt. Expanded rice, the other snack, is made by frying parboiled rice in deep fat or heating it in a current of hot air. The process blows the grains up and makes them porous.

Some other products made from rice grains are glue, starch, sugar, and rice wines. Rice wine is called *sake* in Japan; in India it is known as *arrack*.

The by-products of rice have many industrial uses and are not without food value. The bran and polish layers, when they are fresh and clean, are useful as additions to special types of flour, breakfast cereals, and mixes for pancakes and waffles. A high-grade edible oil something like peanut and cottonseed oils is extracted from rice bran and used in areas where it can be obtained fresh and used quickly. Rice oil does not keep well. The bran left after the oil has been extracted is both a source of B vitamins and a nutritious stock feed that keeps better than bran feed containing oil. Rice polish, the layer under the bran, can be used to thicken gravies and sauces, to make puddings, in sausage stuffings, and in making buttons and soap.

Hulls from milled rice are mixed with ground corncobs to make a soft grit cleaner, used in factories to clean and polish various metals. They are used also as a fuel, as bedding for poultry, for packing, insulation, and as a conditioner in fertilizers. In rolling mills, rice hulls spread on a red-hot steel plate burn instantly to a dense ash, insulating the surface so that metals cool more evenly. Sometimes furfural, discussed in the chapter on corn, is made from rice hulls. Burned rice hulls produce an ash which is used as a bleach, as a filler in concrete and bricks, and as a source of sodium silicate in making soap, polishes, and other cleaning agents.

In China and Japan a very fine type of paper is made from rice straws. We also use both hulls and straws for paper pulp and cellulose. Rayon, plastics, ethyl alcohol, films, shatterproof glass, and rubber substitutes can be derived from cellulose. Rice straw is also valuable for feeding and bedding stock, as a soil mulch, and as fertilizer. When cut and threshed by hand, as in many parts of the Orient, it is used for mats, sandals, ropes, brooms, coats and hats, fuel, and roof thatching.

Rice, a newcomer to the shores of North America, has proved its value in a score of fields and is one of our main crops. Some of the best quality rice in the world is grown in the United States, which produces on a ten-year average 42,756,000 bags (100 lb.) a year. However, only the most southern of our states can produce cultivated rice. So before we leave the subject it might be a good idea to consider that country cousin we mentioned earlier.

Wild rice, *Zizania aquatica,* is an annual grass, native to North America, China, and Japan. Although it belongs to the same family as cultivated rice, it is definitely not its plant ancestor.

American wild rice goes by many names, for it was widely known and used by the Indians and by early explorers and colonists. The French mistakenly called it *folle avoine,* for it is not a "wild oat." Indians of the Northwest called it *menomin;* Indian rice and Tuscarora rice are other names for this useful and nourishing wild grain. Its name, or names synonymous with it, has been given to scores of lakes, ponds, rivers, towns, and counties east of the Rocky Mountains, where it grows in almost every state, and to the Indian tribe, the Menominees.

Wild rice is a strikingly beautiful member of the grass family. It grows in comparatively deep water, rising from two to twelve feet above it, with lovely panicles of yellow-green blossoms in early July. Acre upon acre of still waters—ponds, swamps, and lakes—are covered with it, for it thrives in fresh water and even in water that is slightly salt. Heedless of latitude, it grows in the South and in the North, being especially abundant around the Great Lakes, both in the United States and Canada.

In the early autumn purplish spikes of seeds develop at the tips of the panicles. The seeds are slender grains, one-half to three-quarters of an inch long, enclosed in a bearded husk. So delicate are the little stems that hold them that the seeds drop into the water at the lightest touch when they are ripe. For this reason the Indians gather them before they are fully ripe, slipping through the water in their light canoes. The stalks are tilted over the canoes and the seeds are gently knocked off with sticks.

After the wild rice has been harvested, it is dried in the sun or on racks over a slow fire. It is then placed in a pot or tub and threshed with a stick shaped to serve as a pestle and the chaff winnowed away. The Indians store wild rice for their own use as a winter food and sell some of it for distribution to our stores. Because of its scarcity it is very expensive. The yield has never been more than 800 tons in a year, mainly because of the difficulty in harvesting it. But, like ordinary rice, wild rice swells in cooking so that a little goes far. It is high in food value and its flavor is delicate and different. Like the Indians, we add it to soups and stews. It is excellent served with fowl, either as a stuffing or side dish.

Wild rice provides abundant food for wild birds and fish and efforts have been made to cultivate it. However, since it must be planted in water one to three feet deep and harvested by canoe or boat, the grain remains a challenge to American agriculture.

eight

Oats

(Avena sativa)

We cultivate literature on a little oatmeal.

Sydney Smith

When we think of oats and oatmeal we are likely to think of Scotland, that northern land from which so many colonists came as pioneers to America. In Scotland oats, rather than wheat, were long the mainstay of the diet and a sturdy race grew to greatness on oatmeal porridge, and oaten bread and cakes.

The Scots have put up with considerable joking on the subject. In his *Dictionary of the English Language,* the irrepressible Samuel Johnson defined oats as "a grain which is generally given to horses but in Scotland supports the people." To which a Scotsman countered, "Yes, and that is why in England you have such fine horses and in Scotland we have such fine men." In his biography James Boswell notes that Dr. Johnson later admitted that "his definition was meant to vex them" and adds that he found oats "very much used by the people of Dr. Johnson's home town."

Oatmeal today is a top-ranking breakfast food not only in Scotland but in England, the United States, and many European countries. It is inexpensive and nourishing. Oatmeal is richer than whole wheat in fats and proteins, it contains the important vitamin B_1, also minerals such as iron and phosphorus, and has more calories per pound.

Like other cereal grains the oat originated as a wild grass and has been greatly altered by centuries of cultivation. Plant scientists think the grain was first known as a weed among other cereals. The oldest oat grains known were found in Egypt in materials dating to the Twelfth Dynasty. There is no evidence, however, that they were cultivated in Egypt, and they are not mentioned in the Bible or in Mesopotamian records.

There *is* ample evidence of their very ancient use in northwestern

Europe and this leads to the supposition that they were first cultivated in that region. Ancient oat grains have been found at various sites in Switzerland, Germany, Denmark, and France. The species were identified as *Avena sativa* and *A. strigosa* and they were dated to 2000–1000 B.C. From that time to the present there is an unbroken series of finds. Oats seem to have appeared in Britain around 150 B.C., the grains being mixed with larger samples of wheat and barley. They are thought to have arrived as weeds. In Scotland, however, ancient samples are almost entirely oats. It is conjectured that oat culture became important in England after the Anglo-Saxon invasions.

Writings of the Greeks and Romans indicate that they knew oats only as a weed that was sometimes used medicinally, but that the grain was in common use by the German barbarians who grew it and made their porridge of nothing else. De Candolle thought that oat culture was not introduced to Greece and Italy until the latter half of the Roman Empire. From the writings of Galen he learned that oats abounded in parts of Asia Minor where they were fed to horses, and eaten by men when other grains were in short supply.

Vavilov, in his studies of wheat origins, collected samples of emmer at numerous sites where it is still grown—the Basque country in the Pyrenees, Abyssinia, Bulgaria, Asia Minor, the Crimea, the Caucasus, Iran, and parts of Russia. Every sample had admixtures of *Avena* species, including some unique varieties. Vavilov came to speak of oats as the unfailing attendant of emmer and visualized emmer as spreading across the Old World, carrying with it an assortment of oats as weeds. He thought that in northern Europe, when the climate became much colder around 2000 B.C., oats possibly dominated emmer and became an independent crop.

The career of oats as a weed among other cereal plants was bound to influence its evolution. Any mutation that produced nonarticulate florets would have a selective value, since the grains that did not fall to the ground would be harvested with the main crop and planted with it the following year. Some species, with man as an agent of dispersal, spread far from their native homes in this way and new mutants, in new conditions, must have added to the variability of oat species. Wild oats are still found today, spread over broad geographical areas. Plant scientists now think that cultivated oats were derived from two wild species— the common oat, *Avena sativa*, being apparently the principal commercial species originating from the wild oat *A. fatua,* and *A. byzantina* originating from the wild red oat *A. sterilis*. Cultivation of both classes has given rise, strangely enough, to strains resembling *A. fatua*. This amounts to a return of cultivated oats to wild self-propagated forms.

Oats were first grown in North America by Bartholomew Gosnold in 1602. That hardy pioneer built a hut on one of the Elizabeth Islands

off the New England coast and planted wheat and oats to secure his claim. During the next fifty years the crop was established along the eastern seaboard, and by the middle of the eighteenth century oats had become a very important crop. Production and consumption increased during the nineteenth century. During the last thirty years of the twentieth century it became stabilized at 1100 to 1500 million bushels a year. Today we have more than a thousand different oat strains. Varieties of *Avena sativa* cover the largest acreage. They grow in the cooler climates while varieties of *A. byzantina* (red oats) are grown chiefly in warmer regions.

Oats are being cross bred constantly to improve their quality and yield and to keep ahead of diseases. In the 1940's Victoria-Richland crosses represented a triumph in plant breeding. The grain was excellent and the plants were highly resistant to smuts and rusts. The end of these varieties was foreshadowed in 1946 when an unknown disease, later called Victoria blight, began to appear in all oat varieties carrying the Victoria genes, or hereditary units. By 1948 the disease had become so destructive that farmers did not dare to plant Victoria crosses for fear of complete crop failure. Fortunately, plant scientists had kept busy with their crosses and the Bond variety from Australia was indicating high promise as a parent strain. Crosses with D-69, Iogold, Rainbow, and Anthony were outstanding for high quality grain and not susceptible to Victoria blight. Clinton, Benton, and later Bonda, Zephyr, Mindo, Mohawk, Cherokee, and Advance followed. They yielded bumper crops of grain of a quality unequaled even by the Victoria strains.

Trouble came again in 1951 when a new race of leaf rust and a new race of stem rust appeared on the Bond crosses. These diseases spread widely during 1952 and in 1953 the oat crop suffered its lowest average yield since the drought year of 1934. The estimated loss in the north central states was around $250,000,000. Plant scientists then came forward with new high-yielding, fine quality varieties that were resistant to all known races of stem rust and smut, all prevalent races of crown rust, and to several minor diseases. Among these were derivatives from Landhafter, Santa Fe, and Hajira-Joanette. And so the complicated story goes. How plant diseases spread and the intricacies involved in developing resistant varieties are outlined in another chapter.

Oats rate fourth among our cereal grains, outranked only by wheat, rice, and corn. The plants thrive in most areas of the temperate zone. Although they prefer a moist cool climate, some varieties are grown successfully quite far south. They are not adapted to the tropics, nor will the grain ripen as far north as barley does. Oats do not require special soil conditions, provided the land is not too wet, and often flourish in regions which cannot support other crops. Next to rye, oats have the lowest soil requirements of any grain.

In the United States, oats are grown in the corn belt in rotation with corn and clover, and in all of the areas that produce winter wheat. Iowa, Minnesota, Illinois, and Wisconsin are the most important oat-producing states. The United States grows most of the world's crop. Other important oat growing countries are Canada, Germany, France, Poland, England and Wales, Sweden, Denmark, Argentina, and Russia.

Oat plants grow from two to five feet tall and have long, slender leaves. The leaves are different from those of all other cereals because they do not have auricles at the base of the leaf blade. The flowers are produced in a loose, delicately branching head, each on its own small stem.

Oats are planted either in the spring or fall, depending on the climate. They may be sown broadcast or planted with a seed drill on land that has been suitably cultivated. They make an excellent cover crop and in the early grass stage can be used for pasturage, fodder, or hay. Three months or more are required to produce ripened grain.

Sometimes the plants are clipped in the green grass stage, processed into pellets, and marketed chiefly as animal feed. The pellets are rich in vitamins, especially carotene and Vitamin K, and high in chlorophyll and other food elements.

In spite of the popularity of oats as a breakfast food, only about four per cent of our oat crop, some 50,000,000 bushels, is used for cereal. Most of the rest is fed to farm animals and poultry. In addition to their value as a food, oat by-products that once were wasted have many new and important industrial uses. Flour milled from oats also is playing an interesting role in our food industry.

Oatmeal for cereal use originally was made by cutting the husked grain or groat into several small pieces. Ferdinand Schumacher of Akron, Ohio, later called "the Oatmeal King," was the first to package it for sale in 1854. His product was known as steel-cut, or Scotch, oatmeal and it was packed in glass jars. Later oatmeal was packed and shipped in wooden barrels to retail grocers, who scooped it out and sold it by the pound. Rolled oats were introduced toward the end of the nineteenth century and cardboard cartons then came into use. The first rolled oats were made by rolling the husked kernels without cutting them up and the flakes produced were rather thick and took a long time to cook. Later the grains were cut into several pieces and then rolled. This method produced thinner flakes which required less cooking. Today we can buy still thinner flakes that can be prepared in a few minutes. All three types are equally nourishing. The English call their breakfast oatmeal "porridge"; we sometimes call it "mush," and the Irish name is "stirabout." Many attractive cookies and small cakes can be made with oatmeal and, mixed with wheat flour, it makes tasty muffins and bread.

Today's breakfast oatmeal is prepared and packaged in large factories, which have staffs of food experts and research scientists intent upon producing the best product possible. The oats are bought in carload lots and processed very carefully. The first step is to clean them. Then the grains are dried and toasted to improve their flavor and loosen the husks so that they can be removed more easily. In the next operation the oats are graded as to size. They are hulled with hulling stones which, though mechanically operated, require the service of expert millwrights to get the pressure just right. The hulled grains are separated carefully from the unhulled grains and are steamed, cut, rolled, and packaged—all by machinery. It takes about thirteen and a half bushels of good to excellent oats to produce one barrel of high grade rolled oats, so careful is the processing.

Milling oats for use as a breakfast food leaves great heaps of hulls at the factory as well as tons of broken bits and grains of substandard quality. There are many uses for these by-products so that they no longer are used merely as a fuel or packing material. Some of the parts left when oatmeal is made are used in millfeeds for cattle, sheep, and horses. Oat hulls, mixed into poultry rations, prevent certain diseases and help the birds to develop good feathers. There are also many industrial uses for both oats and hulls.

T. R. Stanton, top ranking expert on oats of the Bureau of Plant Industry, points to one use when he says: "The farm boy of a half century ago was familiar with the custom of occasionally washing or rinsing with oatmeal water the inside of the glazed clay jug in which he carried fresh water from the well to the harvest hands in the fields. It was believed that the water in which oatmeal had been soaked had some cleansing or purifying quality that kept the jug sweet and clean. Now we find oat flour being used in foods, on food packages, and on women's skin, all for the purpose of preserving sweetness."

So, as Grandma suspected when she swished her oatmeal bag through the bath water, oats have been proved to be an excellent cleansing agent. Grandma also was convinced that oatmeal water was an aid to beauty, curing minor skin rashes, blemishes, and sunburn. She was right again. A great deal of oatmeal is used today in making high quality facial soaps, and oat gum, a part of the grain, is prescribed for use in the bath water in treating certain skin diseases.

In the food industry oat flour is playing a role of increasing importance. It contains what scientists call an antioxidant, a substance that preserves the quality of foods containing fats and oils by delaying rancidity caused by the action of oxygen in the air. Today oat flour is being mixed into fatty foods such as peanut butter, margarine, and lard, and dusted over potato chips and salted nuts to keep them pure and sweet. It is also being added to special papers for wrapping or containing such foods as butter, coffee, and bacon. Oat flour and oat gum also help preserve milk, ice cream and other dairy products, fish, meats, powdered egg yolks, and ready mixes for cakes, pie crust, biscuits, cookies, and griddle cakes.

Recently it was announced that a long standing problem of the candy industry had been solved by oat flour. Butter candies are everyone's favorite, but they have been a difficulty to both confectioners and retailers because they cannot be refrigerated and, at room temperatures, develop a rancid taste within two to nine weeks. If such candies are not sold quickly they are a dead loss. Department of Agriculture scientists, working with the National Confectioners Association, found that adding a little oat flour to butter candies—as little as three per cent—made them keep for sixteen to nineteen weeks even in hot weather. The small amount of oat flour used did not affect the flavor of the candy.

About 210,000 tons of oat hulls are left each year from milling oatmeal and oat flour. The main use of these is in the manufacture of furfural. One ton of oat hulls will make about 200 pounds of furfural. The uses of this amber-colored fluid are described in the chapter on corn. Oat straws are used as stock feed and sometimes in making paper, though they are less valuable for paper than wheat and rye straws.

Thus oats, once used only as a food for men and animals, have found new and valuable roles to play in this age of science. From tip to root there is a use for every part of this important cereal plant, which at first grew as a weed among other cereal grasses.

Some Other Grains

. . . *look into the seeds of time and say*
which grains will grow and which will not.

William Shakespeare

In North America we are fortunate in having a climate so varied that all the grains man uses can be planted and grown. Therefore we grow mainly those we like the best.

Across Europe, Asia, and Africa, however, vast areas are too cold, too hot, or too dry for growing wheat, corn, rice, oats, or barley. But there are more than 5,000 species of grass and among them prehistoric men, scattered over semiarid, tropical, and frozen regions of the world, soon found which grains would grow and which would not.

In lands of little rain they planted drought-resistant millets and sorghums, in the steaming tropics other adapted varieties of these versatile grasses. In the cold areas of northern Europe and Asia they grew rye. Where the soil was so sour and unproductive that no other crop would grow, they planted buckwheat and used it as a grain, though it is not a true grain. These plants are not well known to most of us but they are planted in our country for special uses. They are very important in other parts of the world, where they are the main food source for millions of people.

Rye, *Secale cereale,* the most winter-hardy cereal grain known, is a vital crop in the cold northern regions surrounding the Baltic Sea and the Gulf of Finland. It will grow in sandy, infertile soil which will not support other crops and it can be planted continuously in the same place without depleting the soil. It can be grown beyond the area of the hardiest wheat—in the northernmost parts of North America, Europe, and Asia. Rye flourishes as far north as the Arctic Circle and in dry mountain altitudes 14,000 feet above the sea.

The heavy black bread of Russia and Germany is made of rye flour. In nourishment it runs a close second to wheat. In Sweden rye cakes

71

provide a dependable source of food during the cold winters. They are baked twice a year and will keep indefinitely when they have been dried. Black bread has a sour taste which is due to the fermentation of sugars in the flour. Sweet rye bread, however, is also made.

Several kinds of rye have been found growing wild but its true ancestor is not known. It is believed to have originated in the dry regions of southwestern Asia. There is no mention of it in ancient Mediterranean

or Chinese writings, and no trace of it has been found in the Swiss lake dwellings or early Egyptian monuments. Old languages of northern Europe, however, had a name for rye, so probably it was first cultivated in that area.

A disease of rye, called ergot, is poisonous to men and animals. It is caused by the fungus *Claviceps purpurea* which grows parasitically on ears of rye and, less extensively, on those of other grains and grasses. During the Middle Ages ergot was the cause of a terrible disease called St. Anthony's fire, or *ignis sacer,* which periodically scourged Europe, killing thousands. The victims seemed to be selected at random and a frightened populace attributed it to a judgment of God. When the trouble was traced to the fungus, the "holy fire" was forever smothered. One had only to destroy all blasted heads when milling flour from rye. Today ergot derivatives have important medical uses.

Rye is usually sown in the fall and only one or two cultivated species are recognized. The strong tough stems have a bluish-green cast and may reach a height of seven or eight feet on good soil. The head consists of alternately ranked, fairly dense, closely arranged spikelets. Numerous fibrous roots secure the plant, entering the soil more deeply than do those of other grains.

In the early grass stage rye is sometimes cut to provide food for cattle, or used for grazing. Many farmers plant it as a cover crop. In the northern hemisphere rye is often grown in rotation with other crops, since it ripens early and can be harvested in June or July.

In addition to its use in bread making, rye is distilled to make alcoholic drinks. Most of the rye raised in the United States is used for malt and whiskey. The Dutch make gin of it and the Russians a mild beer called *kvass.* The hulls and parts of the grain that are left when flour is milled are mixed with other grains for cattle feed.

Rye straws are too tough and fibrous to be fed to cattle, but are used for bedding. They are also used around the world for making paper and cardboard, for thatching houses, for horse collars, mattresses, and hats.

Sorghum, *Sorgum vulgare,* is a canelike grass which resembles the tall varieties of maize. The stem, however, is more slender and the plant does not produce ears. The stalks range in height from two to sixteen feet and the leaves, two or two-and-a-half feet long, are coated with a waxy whitish bloom. At the tip of the stalk is a heavy head of flowers, or seeds, which may be arranged either loosely or closely in their spikelets. The seeds are smaller than wheat and vary in size, shape, and color. They may be ellipsoid, rounded, or flattened, and colored white, yellow, red, or brown. The husks are mostly straw colored, but some are red, brown, or black.

Sorghum has been known and cultivated from the remotest times. It is believed to be a native of Africa but was known also in ancient China. Sorghum is Africa's most important cereal; it is grown from coast to coast and from Cairo to Capetown. It is widely grown also in India, North China, Manchuria, the United States, and to a lesser extent in Russia, Persia, Arabia, Argentina, and Australia. Sorghums adapt themselves easily to various conditions of soil and climate but prefer warm regions. They are highly resistant to heat and drought and are therefore extremely valuable in arid lands. There are hundreds of varieties.

Sorghums are planted for grain, forage, sirup, and brooms. Four agronomic groups are recognized: sorgos, grain sorghums, grass sorghums, and broomcorn. Subgroups of the grain sorghums are milo, kafir, feterita, shallu, kaoliang, durra hegari, and miscellaneous. The word "sorghum" is most often used to mean sweet sorghums, those from which sirup is made. Most of the grain sorghums grown in the United States are dwarf types suitable for harvesting with a combine harvester-thresher. Hybrid sorghums also are being grown on a field scale.

In food value sorghum grain is very similar to Indian corn and about ninety per cent as nourishing. The protein content is a little higher, the fat content a little lower. As a food the grain is ground into meal and made into porridge, bread, or cakes which the South Africans call "mealies." Sometimes the whole grains are puffed or popped. Throughout the sweep of Africa the natives like to chew the stems of sweet sorghums for the sugar they contain. In the United States sorghums are grown for making sirup or molasses, but mainly for forage.

To make the sirup, the stalks are stripped of their leaves after the seeds have ripened and the top of the plant has been cut off. The stalks are then cut close to the ground and fed through heavy rollers which extract the sap. The sap is boiled in shallow pans until it has reached the proper thickness. Sugar also can be made from sorghum but this is not done on a commercial basis because alcohol, which is expensive, is needed to make the sirup crystallize. It is easier and cheaper to use sugarcane. The shortage of sugar in the North during the War Between the States made sorghums important in the United States in the 1860's. Five years after the plant was introduced from China in 1860, nearly seven million gallons of sirup were made. Since then the amount has climbed steadily.

In addition to its basic value as a livestock feed sorghum finds many uses in industry and manufacture. A wax obtained from its shiny seed coatings is similar to the hard wax obtained from the leaves of the carnauba palm of the tropics. This is used in furniture and shoe polishes and in making carbon paper, sealing wax, and electric insulators. Grain and industrial alcohol can be made from sorghum seed and also butyl alcohol, an ingredient of lacquer solvents and 2,4-D weed killers. Distillers and manufacturers of malt beverages also use many tons of sorghum grain.

Sorghum grain sometimes doubles for tapioca. Starch made from it is used in food products, adhesives, and sizing for both paper and cloth. Oil from the seeds can be used for salad dressings. Perhaps the strangest use of sorghum starch is in digging oil wells. Mixed with a few other substances and enough water to make a slushy mud, the starch is circulated through the bit as the oil well is dug. It cools and lubricates the drill, makes removal of the cuttings easy, and seals the walls so that water will not seep in. A ton or more of sorghum starch is used every time an oil well is dug.

We cannot leave the sorghums, in their bewildering variety, without further note of broomcorn, a type that develops a head made up of many long slender branches in the form of a brush. The heads are bunched together and tied to make brooms and whiskbrooms. About seven varieties of broomcorn are grown in North America. These are classified as standard, western dwarf, and whisk dwarf. No one knows where broomcorn originated, but it has been grown in Europe for 300 years. Benjamin Franklin is believed to have been the first person to plant it in the United States. The first commercial crop was produced here in 1797 on a farm near Hadley, Massachusetts.

The name "millet" in common usage is applied rather indiscriminately to a wide range of cereal plants belonging to distinct genera and even subfamilies of *Gramineae.* The word is derived from the Latin *mille,* a thousand, indicating the fertility of these plants.

There are four different plant species known as millet that are grown
as grains for human food in different parts of the world. The most widely
used one is the nutritious and palatable foxtail millet, *Setaria italica.*
Common millet, *Panicum miliaceum,* with larger grains, is also called
Indian millet, hog millet, broomcorn millet, and proso.

Echinochloa crusgalli variety *frumentacea* goes by the name of Japanese or barnyard millet. Pearl millet, *Pennisetum glaucum,* sometimes
called cat-tail millet, is the fourth category. In the Sudan, pearl millet is
second only to grain sorghum as a food. Some plants called millets are

not millets at all, but are *Sorgum vulgare,* an even more remotely related
species.

The ancestors of foxtail millet are believed to have grown wild in
Egypt and Arabia, from where they spread far eastward and northwest-
ward. As a food plant foxtail millet has been cultivated from prehistoric
times in Egypt, many parts of Asia, and southern Europe. Today it includes many varieties, such as Kursk, Golden Wonder, Turkestan, Si-
berian, Hungarian, and German. Though in the United States it is
cultivated mostly as a forage grass, in other parts of the world this millet
is grown as a food staple to nourish about one-third of the world's population. In the dry regions of India alone, some 35,000,000 acres are
planted in *Setaria.*

This millet is an erect plant from two to five feet high, many stemmed, with an abundance of dense, rich foliage and long, slender, compact spikes. The small ripe grains are encased in shiny hulls that may be colored yellow, red, white, gray, or black. They are highly nourishing and in countries where table use is made of them they appear in the form of meal or groats. Mixed with wheat flour, ground millet makes excellent bread. The stalks of this cereal grass make fine hay and the seeds are sometimes ground for use as stock feed. Millet is used widely as poultry feed and is especially suitable for chicks and pet birds.

To buckwheat, *Fagopyrum,* we shall give but a passing nod. It is not a wheat—not even a grain or a grass. Its fruit is a three-sided achene that resembles a beechnut and from this fact it gets its name. In Old English "buck" meant "beech." Buckwheat is a shallow-rooted, fast-growing annual belonging to the plant family that includes dock and smartweed. The French call it "Saracen wheat" because the Saracens, or Moors, are believed to have brought it to Europe via Spain during their invasion of Europe. Buckwheat is used for pancake flour in North America. In other countries buckwheat flour is used for thin cakes, crumpets, puddings, and a variety of dishes.

Rye, sorghum, and millet—not popular food grains in the New World —still find an important place in our economy. To millions of people in other climates they are the staff of life, growing where other cereals often cannot flourish.

ten

Grain Insects and Diseases

Be ye ashamed, O ye husbandmen; howl, O ye
vinedressers, for the wheat and for the barley;
because the harvest of the field is perished.

Joel I

In the days of long ago, when cereal crops were blasted by disease or devastated by insects, farmers prayed to Ceres, Demeter, or Bertha, and propitiated the elves and corn spirits that might be abroad in the fields. The corn spirit might be a "grass wolf," "corn wolf," or "rye wolf." His passage was noted when the wind bent the ripening grain. Sometimes he masqueraded as a satyr-like creature. There were also gods of the wind and rain.

These picturesque creatures were banished to the realm of fantasy when new instruments and new knowledge led men to examine the farmer's problems more closely. Today's farmer insures the best crop possible by keeping in touch with his state agricultural station so that he can plant disease-resistant strains and fight insects with the newest weapons available.

Thousands of years before Christ, hordes of grasshoppers, which the Egyptians called locusts, periodically destroyed crops in the Nile valley just as they did in the Mississippi valley in 1874–1875 and in the Dakotas in 1932. Once, very long ago—before man appeared—insects dominated the world, and a great entomologist, in a moment of despair, said he believed they would again. The multiplication of pests, he said, is encouraged by planting large areas in a single crop. Then, too, we have upset the balance of nature by importing diseased and insect-infested plants from other continents. The European corn borer, the Japanese beetle, and the Hessian fly are only a few of the destructive grain and turf pests brought to North America from Europe and Asia. The enemies they had in their homelands were lacking here, the food supply was unlimited, and they swarmed rapidly over our farmlands and gardens. Today we have strict plant quarantine laws which are designed to bar unwanted insects and diseased plants and prevent the spread of those already here, but with distances shortened by ship and plane the hazards are greatly increased. However, insects will not control the world again if our scientists can help it.

The war against insects that attack our crops is without truce, but before sketching some of the battle methods we must be aware that relatively few insects are serious pests. Of about 600,000 known kinds, only about 10,000 are a real problem. Many are beautiful, most are harmless, and some are vitally important. Bees, wasps, butterflies, and other groups distribute pollens and so help to insure the production of many useful seeds and fruits. Some insects are associated so closely with particular trees and plants that fruiting cannot take place without them. Still others, such as the praying mantis and the ladybug beetle *Vedalia,* kill serious pests.

In fighting insects that attack our cereal crops we have to use every weapon that can be mobilized. Farmers spend about $375,000,000 a year on insecticides and consider the money well spent when they harvest bigger and better crops. The development of the highly effective chlorinated hydrocarbons and organic phosphorous toxicants and methods of applying them have been phenomenal during the last decade. They have, for instance, revolutionized the control of grasshoppers, being so successful that they have completely replaced poisoned bait, the standard control for half a century.

The chlorinated hydrocarbons have also received general acceptance as controls for soil insects. Soil insecticides are used in two ways. One is to apply them to the soil as spray, dust, or granular formulations; the other is to use them as a dressing or coating on seeds. The use of soil insecticides for the control of rootworms on grain crops in the United States probably involves more treated acres than any other soil insect control program. Aldrin, heptachlor, dieldrin, and BHC are the leading rootworm insecticides. Since most of these preparations are not translocated within the plant, soil treatments can be used without obtaining any objectionable residues in the above-ground parts of the plant.

The application of chlorinated hydrocarbon insecticides to the above-ground parts of grain plants for insect control has limited use because of residue problems. However, a large amount of these insecticides is used on corn and small grains with certain restrictions on the use of forage for livestock feed, or a restricted period of time between application and harvest.

Other control methods seek to restore the balance between insects and plants. One phase of this type of control is to search out and use insect enemies of individual pests, and diseases that help stabilize them in their land of origin. Cultural methods and the development of resistant plant strains also are in this category. Behind each control method tested are months and years of painstaking work because the life history of the insect must be known completely before an effective weapon can be devised. The search for parasites and diseases, their testing, breeding, and introduction is also difficult. Sometimes startling success crowns the entomologists' effort, but often, for climatic and other reasons, the parasites fail to establish themselves in American fields or gradually die out.

Shortly after the European corn borer was discovered (1917) nibbling away in Massachusetts, the search for a biological control got under way in France. Entomologists scoured Europe for natural enemies of the pest. Between 1920 and 1938 nearly 24,000,000 hibernating borers were collected in the field and imported for study. Some of these contained parasites in their early stages, as well as cocoons, puparia, and pupae of the parasite species. Eighteen distinct species were obtained in Europe. The search was continued in Japan, Korea, and Manchuria, and between 1929 and 1936 thirteen more parasite species were found. Others, added from time to time, brought the total to twenty-four. After exhaustive testing, six species were successfully colonized and have become established in corn-producing states, where they are busily at work, achieving destruction of from forty-five to seventy-five per cent of the corn borer population.

In contrast to the favorable experience with corn borer parasites, the natural enemies of the sugarcane borer have failed in Louisiana and Florida because they could not survive the cold weather that comes periodically to those states.

Efforts to control grasshoppers, the Hessian fly, and chinch bugs—all serious enemies of the grasses—by means of parasites and diseases have also been unsuccessful or indecisive. But ranchers and entomologists alike are now watching with interest the progress of an internal parasite, *Anagyrus antoninae,* which has been brought from Hawaii to fight Rhodes grass scale. This pest of range grasses has destroyed completely thousands of acres of excellent stands of Rhodes grass in southeastern

Texas and is spreading rapidly. It attacks not only Rhodes grass but several other valuable forage grasses.

Sometimes insects can be controlled by special cultural methods. The corn ear worm, European corn borer, and corn rootworm—the three worst pests of 350 that attack corn—can be kept pretty well in hand by clean culture and crop rotation. Clean culture means cutting and shredding for fodder, or completely destroying, every part of the corn plants remaining above ground after harvest, then plowing the stubble under

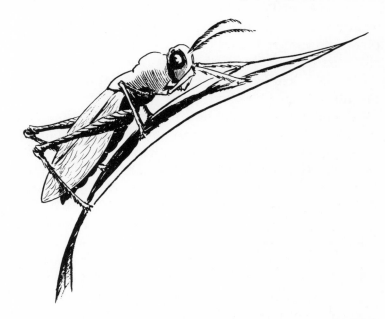

or burning it. This treatment destroys insect pests that live above the ground. If a different crop is planted the following year the root pests cannot survive.

Another example of natural control involves the Hessian fly. This insect invaded North America as a stowaway in the bedding straw of German soldiers who were paid by the British to help them in the Revolutionary War. It is one of the worst pests of our wheat fields and American farmers have been fighting it ever since the republic was established. Within recent years a control was worked out which was based upon the fact that the Hessian fly lays its eggs on the young green shoots of wheat planted in the fall. If seeding is delayed they cannot find a place to lay their eggs. A schedule of "safe planting" dates has now been worked out for every area of the United States where winter wheat is grown, in an effort to reduce the damage caused by this pest.

For some strange reason insects do not seem to attack certain varieties of wheat and other grains. This fact has led to another phase of research, the improvement of insect-resistant strains and the development of additional varieties that are not appetizing to insect pests.

Traps of different types, baited with odorous materials attractive to particular insects, or with lights of a color to lure unsuspecting night flyers, are used in making surveys of insect emergences. Behind the odor used to lure a given pest lie years of study and experimentation with both plant and insect. Lights used in conjunction with traps have not been based on guesswork either. Night flying insects have their preferences as to wave length and intensity of radiation. Generally speaking they like ultraviolet, blue, and green light better than yellow, red, or infrared. Among odorous materials preferred by various insects are geraniol, sassafras, and a fermenting mixture of sugar and malt.

Some traps are used by farmers with considerable success in control work, but usually only until better methods are found. In such case a poison may be used in connection with them. A "hopperdozer," however, depends almost entirely upon mechanical action. Designed to trap insects that hop or jump, it consists of a long narrow and shallow trough made of boards or metal backed by a vertical shield about three feet high that is partly filled with kerosene-coated water. When the insects fly up to avoid the hopperdozer they hit the shield and meet their end in the water. Chinch bugs are among the crawling insects that can be trapped in deep dusty-sided furrows plowed across their path as they move from one field to another. The loose dust prevents them from crawling out, and post holes, dug at intervals along the furrows, trap them as they try to escape. Kerosene, or a heavy stick, is then used to destroy them.

The entomologist uses traps to keep a careful check on build-ups of dangerous pests in different areas, and on new infestations. Weather conditions and many other factors are involved in the severity of each year's attack and for this reason entomologists in all states are ever on the alert. They warn farmers by press and radio and are in close touch with agents of the United States Department of Agriculture. Every week government entomologists, working with country-wide information, issue a national report that goes to newspapers and agricultural leaders all over the country.

Grain in storage is attacked by a different class of insects and requires a different sort of protection. This phase is of vast importance. Every year stored grain insects destroy about a million tons of wheat alone—on farms, in homes, mills, and grain elevators—enough to provide everyone in the United States with seven weeks' supply of bread.

In large scale storage and shipment four species of insects cause almost all of the damage. These are the granary weevil, the rice weevil, the lesser grain borer, and the *Angoumois* grain moth. All of these can break open

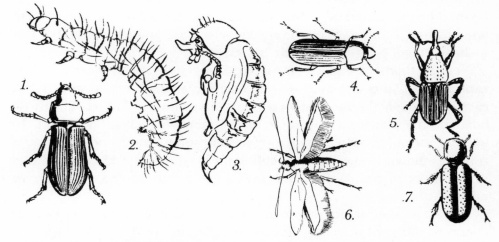

Some Insect Pests of Grains. 1. Cadelle beetle. 2. Indian meal moth. 3. Broad-horned flour beetle pupa. 4. Slender-horned flour beetle. 5. Granary weevil. 6. Angoumois moth. 7. Lesser grain borer.

the kernels. Once this happens, other species move in to increase the damage. Many pests feed only on the surface of the kernels or in grain dust. These can be controlled by cleaning the grain.

Modern elevators, where grains are graded and stored, have very efficient machinery for screening out insects and broken or damaged kernels. However, they cannot reach all of the insects, especially those that are inside the grain, and other methods must be used. Some can be killed by heat, others by cold. In certain cases fumigants are used. Most stored grain pests are of subtropical origin and cannot stand cold. They become inactive at temperatures below 50 degrees Fahrenheit and are killed if the mercury goes much lower. If the weather outside is cold enough, insects in grain can be controlled or destroyed by pouring the grain from one bin into another, or by dropping it through chilled air.

In a similar way grain insects can be killed by raising the temperature of the grain in driers. A temperature of 140 degrees Fahrenheit will kill all grain infesting insects. Drying the grain also helps, because insects cannot survive if the moisture content of the grain falls below eight per cent.

Fumigants are used when other methods fail or are impractical. There are a number of different kinds and great care is required in handling them. The usual method is to spray them on the grain as it is run from one bin into another. When the grain has been aired thoroughly after such treatment it is perfectly safe to use.

New methods of insect control are being sought constantly. In one experiment plants are treated with chemicals which are absorbed and carried through the roots, stems, leaves, and flowers. The chemicals do not hurt the plants but kill some of the insects which attack them. In another area of investigation the effects of radiant energy on insect pests is being studied in the hope of finding an inexpensive and effective way to kill insects in grain, wood, and textiles without damaging the materials infested.

Three types of radiant energy have been used in experiments; electric energy of different wavelengths such as radio, infrared, visible and ultra-violet, gamma rays, and X-rays; audible and ultrasonic sound waves; and atomic energy such as from neutrons, alpha particles, and electrons. High frequency radio waves killed rice weevils in wheat by raising their body temperature. Infrared rays have destroyed insects in grain by a similar action, and cathode rays killed larvae of the flour beetle in a very thin layer of flour. This work, however, is still very much in the experimental stage. Sound waves usually do not penetrate materials deeply enough to be effective; high frequency waves tend to shatter the infested material along with the insect; and radio and infrared rays are too expensive. But the experiments point to future developments that may be spectacular.

Grains and other grasses are subject to many diseases which until comparatively recent times were not understood. In an earlier day, when farms were small and crops diverse, farmers took a loss in one area, philosophically, and profited on another. With mechanized agriculture came large scale farming and concentration of a single crop on vast acreages. This type of farming made control of ravaging diseases vitally important since serious crop failures could affect whole regions and bring national and international economic repercussions.

Before the role of microorganisms was known, crop failures were often blamed on the weather, which actually can be a factor in the development and spread of disease. Later it was noted that fungi seemed always to be associated with the appearance of blasted plants. At first the fungi were thought to be the result rather than the cause of the trouble. Nevertheless the fungi were studied and classified. Then Prévost and later De Bary proved by experiments the nature of parasitism, the epidemic character of fungus diseases, and the need for controls. Thus was born the science of plant pathology.

To control the hundreds of fungi-induced smuts, rusts, rots, and mildews that attack the grasses and other plants, the phytopathologist must know in detail the structure and life cycle of the parasitic plants that cause them, as well as the structure and life cycle of the plants attacked. Even then, in studying a disease, he may not solve the problem, because it may be bacterial in origin, caused by a virus with an insect carrier involved, or a deficiency disease induced by the lack of some plant nutrient.

In this comparatively new field, dedicated workers spend hours over microscopes studying plant structure and disease-causing organisms. New diseases materialize even as they work and sometimes assume frightening proportions. A disease apparently vanquished by resistant plants may appear in a new and menacing guise, altered to meet the challenge of existence. The war must be unending for there is little hope that any fungus disease can be routed completely. The breeding of resistant plants and the use of fungicides and insecticides are important weapons in the war against the diseases of cereal grasses. Chemicals which, applied to the plant, enter its system, together with new equipment to apply the chemicals, are a possible future form of control.

The two most important groups of diseases attacking cereal plants are rusts and smuts. General information about them gives a glimpse into the complex field of plant pathology. Both groups are caused by tiny fungi that live on the plants, stealing their food and weakening or killing them. The plant on which the fungi live is called a *host* and the tiny plants are parasites. Losses from fungus diseases, resulting from a lower amount and poorer quality of grain, run into millions of dollars every year.

Wheat, oats, and barley are very susceptible to fungus diseases, but rice, corn, and rye are attacked too. The fungi are spread by spores. These microscopic dust-like particles are scattered far and wide by infected seeds, by the wind, and by the feet of birds and insects.

Of the two main types, smut fungi are easier to control because their life cycle is simpler. Spores of some smut fungi cling to the seeds of infected plants. When the seeds sprout they enter the plants, growing with them and replacing the seed head with smutty, often foul-smelling masses of spores that spread to other seeds during threshing and handling. Other smut fungi produce spores that are blown about in the air, contact the host plant, and infect its tissues. Still others infect the flowers so that when the seed is formed it already contains the fungus.

Rusts differ from smuts in requiring two host plants. They live first on one and then on the other. There are hundreds of different rusts and smuts that attack grains and other grasses. Some affect the leaf, some the stem, others the root, or the seed head. Stem rust, one of the most destructive, has about sixty forms. It attacks wheat, oats, barley, rye, and perhaps a hundred grasses. Stem rust develops on barberry leaves, the infective spores being produced by masses of small orange-colored cups. From these it spreads to grains and grasses.

There are several methods used in controlling the diseases of grain plants. Sometimes a change in the schedule of crop rotation, or of planting dates, will help. Scab, for example, attacks both wheat and corn. In areas where infection is severe the best solution of the problem is simply not to plant wheat after corn. Spores of the fungus that causes scab live on old cornstalks during the winter and are scattered over the young wheat plants in the spring. If wheat *must* be planted after corn where scab exists, the cornstalks should be removed from the field or plowed under completely.

The breeding of disease-resistant strains to meet a serious threat is well illustrated by the work done to combat a stem rust designated as "Race 15B" which began to ravage the durum wheats in North Dakota, Minnesota, and other states in 1950. By 1953 it had spread so fast that sixty-five per cent of the crop was lost; by 1954, loss was seventy-five per cent. Research agronomists of the United States Department of Agriculture, in the spring of 1954, were ready with rust-resistant Willet, a cross between a Brazilian wheat called Frontana and another named Thatcher. Seeds were available for general planting in the infested region a year later. By spring 1956 four new resistant varieties had been bred and seeds were available for planting on some 150,000 acres in the main durum-producing areas of North Dakota. The problem was believed solved. Race 15B attacks other wheats but concentrated on the durums because they mature later.

Breeding new varieties often takes a long time but the agronomists in this instance went to work on the heels of the first devastating outbreak of Race 15B. They made their first crosses in greenhouses during the winter of 1950–1951, selecting 15B resistant wheats from the United States Department of Agriculture's world collection and susceptible but adaptable durum varieties. Field experiments in the autumn of 1951 yielded about 2,500 seeds from promising crosses. An almost continuous program of selection enabled the scientists to narrow their field to five promising lines. Five to ten pounds each of the five lines were sown that fall on irrigated government land at Brawley, California. This made possible a winter crop of seeds. From the Brawley plots sufficient seeds were obtained to plant five acres of each of the five lines in the spring of 1954. These seeds were planted in North Dakota. One line proved unsatisfactory and was discarded, but 238 bushels of seed were harvested from the other four lines and these were planted on irrigated land in Arizona. The Arizona crop gave 8,000 bushels of seed. These were planted in North Dakota in the spring of 1955 and resulted in 128,000 bushels of seed. By moving from the greenhouse to the field and then back to the greenhouse, and by managing two extra winter crops in the Southwest, scientists cooperating on the 15B problem achieved two to three plant generations a year, bringing the speediest relief possible to the durum growers. The work is being continued with a careful eye on the northern spring bread wheats and winter wheats of the Central and South Plains, which are susceptible to Race 15B but have not been damaged by it as seriously as the durums.

Meanwhile another plant breeder of the Agricultural Research Service, E. R. Sears, was making seemingly magic passes over various plants such as emmer, Chinese spring wheat, and rust-resistant *Aegilops umbellulata* from the Mediterranean region. His aim was to find a cross that would be resistant to leaf rust. There are twenty-two races of leaf rust and very few varieties of common wheat are resistant to any of them, but some related grasses are almost immune. *Aegilops umbellulata* was one of these, but there was a difficulty. This grass possesses but seven chromosomes—those microscopic rodlike bodies of plant cells that carry hereditary factors—while common wheat has six sets of seven. The goal would have to be approached deviously.

At this point it is necessary to explain that when we say a plant has a single set of chromosomes, we are referring to its reproductive cells: the male cell that comes from the pollen grain and the egg cell in the ovule. When these reproductive cells, called gametes, unite, the new plant that results has two sets of chromosomes, usually alike or nearly so. When this plant in turn reproduces, the two sets in each parent are reshuffled into single sets again for the gametes. So each cell of a mature plant of *Aegilops umbellulata* has two sets of seven; each of its gametes has one set of seven. Common wheat, *Triticum aestivum,* has in each cell of the mature plant six sets of seven; in each gamete three sets.

Dr. Sears first crossed the *Aegilops* species with emmer, a wheat that has fourteen chromosomes in its gametes. The hybrid had fourteen plus seven, or twenty-one chromosomes; and it was sterile, forming no functioning gametes, because the twenty-one chromosomes (three sets, none matching) could not be sorted into two single sets. But when this hybrid was treated with the drug colchicine, each of its twenty-one chromosomes was doubled, so that it had in each cell so affected *six* sets of seven; and each chromosome could be paired with its duplicate so as to make it possible to sort out these six sets into three sets for each gamete. The hybrid was now crossed with Chinese spring wheat, which also has three sets of seven in its gametes.

The three-way hybrid had the proper number of chromosomes now to be crossed with wheat, but only fourteen (those from the emmer) were related to those of wheat closely enough to pair with them in the formation of gametes. The other seven (from *Aegilops*) were different from any in the wheat, so that when the gametes were formed, seven grass and seven wheat chromosomes had no mates and could slip at random into one gamete or the other. Some gametes got as many as six grass chromosomes, others none.

Dr. Sears now back-crossed his emmer-grass-wheat hybrids with Chinese spring wheat, and again back-crossed the new hybrids. Among the resulting plants he found one with forty-three chromosomes (six sets plus one), which resisted leaf rust and generally resembled Chinese spring wheat. However, it was a weak plant of low fertility. One chromosome of this plant—and only one—was ascertained to be from the grass

Aegilops. Offspring of this plant that carried the one odd *Aegilops* chromosome in addition to the twenty-one pairs of wheat chromosomes (six sets) were also rust-resistant, but they continued the weakness and low fertility, that were also tied up with the odd grass chromosome.

In an effort to eliminate the undesirable features of the rust-resistant hybrids, Mr. Sears now X-rayed the plants before flowering time. When the flowers appeared he applied pollen from them to normal wheat plants. X-raying often causes individual chromosomes to break up and exchange their hereditary units, or genes. In this case seventeen of the 6,091 plants that were produced after the X-raying retained the rust resistance of the parent plant but appeared to have only the small part of the grass chromosome that carried rust resistance. One plant in particular had so few undesirable grass features that it apparently had picked up from the middle of the grass chromosome just one tiny section, the gene for rust resistance. This was a stout forty-two chromosome wheat hybrid with near immunity to all twenty-two of the leaf rust races and no other character of the grass in evidence.

A similar story of painstaking work could be told of the war against oat diseases during the last twenty years. The Federal Government spent in that period a little more than $3,000,000 for research leading to resistant varieties. The investment paid a thousand dollars for every three dollars spent in research, with the oat growers profiting to the extent of a billion dollars in added revenue.

In field and laboratory, unceasingly, research scientists seek to keep farmers abreast of the insects and diseases that threaten our vital crops of cereal grains. As the work continues no one knows what triumphs or disasters lie ahead, but never before has the outlook been so encouraging.

eleven

A World Business

. . . let them gather all the food
of those good years . . .

Genesis XLI

Grains became big business early in the nineteenth century when twenty-two-year-old Cyrus McCormick, a Virginia farm boy, invented his harvesting machine. The McCormick reaper could harvest an acre of wheat in two-and-a-half man hours instead of sixty-four. It was probably the greatest farm invention since a leisure loving Egyptian, around 4300 B.C., got the notion of hitching oxen to his plow.

In the wake of the reaper came mechanized gang plows, graders, disk harrows, drills for planting seed, and the combine harvester-thresher. The machines opened the vast prairies to farming. Railroads were strung across the continent, and special warehouses, or grain elevators, were built to handle the harvest. Millions of bushels of wheat from the United States and Canada soon flowed in golden streams to other continents. When more countries entered the grain trade—Argentina, Australia, and Russia—giant business organizations were developed to handle marketing problems, with trading centers in Chicago, Liverpool, Winnipeg, and other great cities. National laws were passed to govern the grain trade inside countries and international agreements regulating the huge enterprise were made between nations.

North American grain is usually handled in bulk. On other continents it is sold in sacks because complete grain elevator systems have not been developed. Grain elevators play a vital part in the grain trade of the United States and Canada. There are two types. Country elevators are small warehouses located along railways of the grain belt. They are equipped to handle up to about 5,000 bushels at a time. Terminal elevators are towering steel and concrete buildings, located at rail and shipping centers, which may hold as many as 10,000,000 bushels in their enormous bins.

90

When grain has been harvested, it is loaded into trucks and taken to the nearest receiving station, which is, of course, a country elevator on a siding, usually owned and operated by a railroad. Here the farmer can sell his grain directly to the owner or manager or have it stored for future sale, possibly at a better price. After he has made his arrangement the grain is emptied into the chute of the elevator. It goes first through a cleaner, which removes bits of grass, dirt, and chaff, and then it is passed into the bottom of the elevator "leg," called the "boot." The leg is a two-chambered tube, centrally located in the elevator, and its job is to unload the grain. Inside the leg there is a bucket loader, an endless belt with buckets attached, each of which holds about a peck of grain. Machinery to operate the belt is in a little cupola on top of the building. The buckets go down through one chamber of the tube and up the other, scooping up the grain and lifting it to the top of the elevator, called the "head." From the head other tubes direct it into storage bins. Each bin has a spout at the bottom, opened and closed by means of a valve and built high enough for a freight car to be run up under it on tracks.

When a freight car is to be loaded with grain, it is moved up under the spout. The grain to be sold is then carried by the leg up to the head of the elevator again, to be measured in a hopper, weighed, and sent to a storage bin. When the valve at the bottom of the storage bin is opened the grain pours from the spout by gravity, quickly filling the freight car. This carload of wheat then joins other cars, collected from sidings all over the grain belt, to form a long train moving across the country to a trading center such as Chicago, Kansas City, or St. Louis. Here it goes to a giant terminal elevator to be processed and stored until it is finally sold.

Terminal elevators are owned by grain and flour companies and by farmers' cooperative associations. They are much more complicated in structure than the small country elevators because they have a much bigger job to do. Here, carefully adjusted and operated machinery again cleans the grain if necessary, weighs it carefully, and perhaps sends it on to be dried or bleached. Other machinery grades the grain under government inspection, then stores it away in enormous cylindrical bins.

Each kind of grain is classified according to type and graded for quality. For instance, there are seven official classes of wheat: hard red spring, durum, red durum, hard red winter, soft red winter, white, and mixed. Each class has five grades. Top grade wheat must weigh at least sixty pounds per bushel, contain no more than two per cent damaged kernels, and not more than six per cent foreign material, including other types of wheat. The lowest grade includes wheat that weighs fifty to fifty-one pounds per bushel, contains up to fifteen per cent damaged kernels, and up to seventeen per cent foreign materials. Grain is usually sold by sample.

At the large terminal elevators the operating machinery, which may be either electric or steam, is often housed in a separate building called a working house. The machinery includes legs designed especially for cleaning, screening, drying, and bleaching grain. Each leg may handle as much as 10,000 bushels of grain an hour. After passing through the different processes in the working house the grain is sent to the storage bins—fireproof cylinders twenty to thirty feet in diameter, often a hundred or more feet high, with walls seven or eight inches thick. There may be over a hundred storage bins. Here the grain is held until it is time to load it for shipment to a mill or to a foreign country.

Elevating machinery used to unload grain at terminal warehouses may be the bucket-loader type or pneumatic. Legs of the bucket-loading type are made so that they can be raised or lowered. They can be lifted high over the side of a big freighter, then lowered forty feet or more to the bottom of the hold. When a ship is being unloaded the leg is dropped down into the grain which is then scooped up by the buckets on the endless belt and into a receiving room. Here another belt takes it to a hopper called a "garner." The garner measures it into weighing machinery located directly below. When it has been weighed, it is dropped through a spout and sent on to cleaning or storage bins.

The pneumatic elevator has no leg. Instead there is a hollow boom, rigged like a crane, with a suction tube at the end, which is swung over the side of the vessel to be unloaded. The tube is flexible and constructed so that it can be shortened or lengthened, telescope fashion. At the inner end a powerful suction pump draws air up through the tube and with it a stream of grain which is directed into a vacuum chamber. From the vacuum chamber other tubes distribute it to the desired bins. When pneumatic machinery is used, grain does not have to be shoveled to any special place to be loaded because the end of the tube can reach all the corners. It does not produce heat and dust, as bucket elevators do, and is therefore better from a health standpoint for men loading grain.

When a train of freight cars is to be unloaded it is run up onto a siding close to the building so that each car stands directly under an elevator leg. Two men in each car, operating steam-driven shovels, scoop the grain into the pits at the base of each leg. The buckets pick it up and take it to the top of the shaft. There they are tipped automatically and the grain goes into the turnhead spouts and on, by gravity, to the garners, the hoppers, perhaps the cleaners, and finally to storage bins.

Marine elevators are used to transfer grain from ships to freight cars. In this operation the elevator legs are swung out from their house and their feet are lowered through the hatchway into the ship's hold. The grain is carried to the top of the elevators where turnhead spouts send it to the bins. The valves at the bottom of the bins are then opened and the grain falls into the waiting freight cars. A freight car holds about 1,200 bushels; it can be loaded in about three minutes. Sometimes marine elevators are mounted on barges so that they can be moved from place to place as needed. They are then called floating elevators.

When a grain ship is to be loaded it is moored securely to the warehouses and its hatches are lifted. Great spouts, extending from the floor valves to the bins, direct the torrent of grain which is delivered by gravity into the ship's hold. The largest freighter can be loaded in from two to three hours.

After grain is accepted by a warehouse the receipts issued to the owner put it into commerce. By transfer of the receipts from one person or group to another the grain is often sold and resold many times before it reaches its final destination. A great deal of grain is handled through boards of trade and international trading associations.

To outline the whole complicated system of the grain trade would require a book in itself. For instance grains, especially wheat, are often sold before they are harvested. This practice is known as trading in futures. Grain traders buy the wheat for shipment and, either immediately or later, sell a similar amount to be delivered at a future period— all by means of receipts and notes. Futures trading originated in the United States at the turn of the century and was adopted quickly by other countries. Today there are eighteen boards of trade and exchanges in the United States which deal in grain and other agricultural futures. New York has four, Chicago three, and others are located in Duluth, Kansas City, Los Angeles, Memphis, Milwaukee, Minneapolis, Portland, Seattle, New Orleans, San Francisco, and St. Louis. Some deal entirely in grain, others in cotton or a combination of products.

By means of an exchange a farmer can sell his crop of wheat or other grain when the price suits him, months before it is reaped. In this way he can avoid financial loss from falling prices. In the same manner a miller can buy a cargo of wheat and sell contracts for future delivery of the flour he intends to make from it. For safe operation exchanges must keep on hand a plentiful supply of the kinds of wheat millers prefer. Safeguards are provided against changes in the market price for both farmers and traders. For instance, each party to a contract must put up an agreed amount of cash to cover such changes. If the price difference is not paid at the time agreed, all contracts held in the name of the defaulting member in the clearing house registry are sold, or purchased, as the case may be. The Grain Futures Act of 1922 put futures trading under government supervision to prevent the price fixing, cornering (getting control of the market so as to manipulate prices), and cheating that marked the early history of the grain exchange.

To keep track of the amounts and quality of different grains that will be produced in any year, a special bureau of the United States Department of Agriculture publishes monthly reports on conditions in the country's grain fields. In March the report gives figures on the amount of grain still in the hands of farmers. In April it sketches the outlook for winter wheat and rye. The May bulletin reports the total acreage where crops have failed and are not worth harvesting and in June figures are given for the growing winter grain and the prospects for spring wheat. In July corn acreages and crop estimates are reported, in September an estimate of the wheat and rye crops, and in October an estimate of the corn crop and spring grains. The December report gives figures for the entire year's grain crop. Grain exchanges and commission houses also get reports from their own men in the grain belt and from commissioned experts traveling through the country to estimate crops and conditions.

In spite of the withdrawal of many acres of land from production, the United States is producing bumper crops of grain due to the development of improved varieties and techniques. The average yield per acre is increasing steadily. Use of hybrid corn in the Midwest has added an extra 500,000,000 bushels to the annual corn crop—on the same land with the same labor. In vast areas that produced eight to twelve bushels of wheat an acre thirty years ago, twelve to fourteen bushels an acre are being harvested today, and sometimes more. A Canadian farmer in recent years announced in a sworn statement that he had averaged eighty-five bushels of wheat on each of twenty acres planted.

American grains are traveling the oceans of the world, helping to nourish people everywhere. Out of our vast supply tons of stored grains are being distributed through United States organizations to feed hungry people of other lands. Under a policy announced in November, 1955, by Secretary of Agriculture, Ezra Benson, eighteen nongovernment agencies began to distribute surplus grain in sixty-seven countries. Like

Egypt of old we have sown, reaped, and stored during the good years and are dividing our rich hoard with others who have not been as fortunate. The amount of grain in government storage when the gift plan was inaugurated had reached a total of 1,500,000,000 bushels.

And with this account of modern trading in wheat and other grains we come to the end of our account of the cereal grasses. But we have not yet finished our story of the grasses because we still have to consider sugarcane and the versatile, beautiful bamboo.

twelve

Giant Grass

(Bambuseae)

. . . each breath of the Southwind
makes a new bamboo.

Po Chü-i

At the dawn of civilization in the Orient men found close at hand a fabulous tribe of grasses—fast growing, often timber sized—whose uses were to be multiplied a thousandfold as the people progressed from primitive living toward one of the world's great cultures. These grasses, the bamboos, are as important today as they were many centuries ago.

Bamboos grow throughout the world in tropical and subtropical regions and some of the hardy species thrive in the temperate zone, but it is in the lands of the East that they grow most luxuriously and have been most appreciated and used. Every continent except Europe has its native species. South Asia is richest in the variety of its native bamboos and the Americas are second, while Africa has very few. The total number of distinct kinds that have been described is estimated to be from six to seven hundred, classified in about sixty genera. About two hundred species, composing eleven genera, are native to the New World and, oddly perhaps, only one of the eleven has been found outside this hemisphere.

The known native bamboos of the United States consist of two species and several varieties of the genus *Arundinaria. Arundinaria gigantea,* the giant southern cane, grows wild in southern Ohio, Indiana, Illinois, Oklahoma, Missouri, and states farther south all the way to east Teaxs, while *A. tecta,* switch cane, grows along the Atlantic and Gulf coastal region from Maryland southward. These native bamboos, which once formed extensive groves or canebrakes and found many uses, have been yielding gradually to agriculture in the fertile southern valleys.

Though some bamboos grow as tall as trees, forming impenetrable forests, and others are slender and small, they are all perennial grasses, sharing the main characteristics of their smaller relatives. Like other grasses they grow very rapidly; unlike them, they live much longer. While many of the perennial grasses die after several years, the bamboos live from twenty to forty years and perhaps even longer. They shed their leaves like deciduous trees and are singularly free of diseases and pests.

Bamboos like a rich deep loam soil and a warm climate, though some grow in areas where the temperature plunges to zero Fahrenheit and below. They reach the snow line of the Andes in South America, 15,000

feet above sea level, and are found at altitudes of 10,000 feet or more in the Himalayas. They differ widely in appearance, size, and habit of growth. There are dwarf bamboos only a few inches high, long slender climbers interlacing forest trees, and giants that reach a height of one hundred to one hundred and twenty feet (the highest recorded measured one hundred and seventy) with culms eight to twelve inches in diameter. Some grow in clumps, others have long, jointed rhizome systems that send up many shoots so that a single plant can form a dense forest.

There are bamboos that bloom every year or every few years and others that bloom only at long intervals. Some have never been known to produce blossoms. But individuals of the same generation always flower at the same time wherever they are. In India one of the largest species, *Bambusa arundinacea,* blooms all along the west coast at intervals of thirty-two years. Such erratic habits make classification of the bamboos a minor nightmare to botanists since, as in other grasses, the flowering branch identifies the species.

In some bamboos the flowers appear on leafy branches; in others the leaves fall from the culms before the flowers appear. Still others develop their flowers on leafless radical stems. The flowering culms of many bamboos die when the seeds ripen and in some species the entire plant dies, down to its very roots, so that reproduction must depend upon dropped seeds. Because the bamboos are so individualistic in their seeding habits they are usually propagated by means of cuttings or divisions.

Like other grasses most of the bamboos have hollow, jointed, glossy stems, usually cylindrical (*Chimonobambusa quadrangularis* has square culms), smooth, and varying in color from pale green to golden. But the beautiful *Phyllostachys nigra* has black stems and Shikotan-chiku, a native of Shikotan Island in the Kuriles, has culms spotted with dark brown—a decorator's delight. In a part of Hunan Province, China, there grows a very curious bamboo with purple rings on the stems. The purple-ringed culms are highly esteemed by Chinese flute makers. According to a very ancient legend, says historian Tsui Chi, the beneficent third ruler of the Chinese nation, Emperor Shun, was touring the Mountains of the Nine Doubts in the wilderness of Ts'ang Wu when he fell ill and died. His two wives mourned over him and shed tears which fell like pearls on the bamboos and never dried. At their death they became the goddesses of the river Hsiang. The modern version of the legend says the tear drops of the empresses marked the bamboos with purple rings, and the plaintive music of the purple-ringed flutes echoes the wind, mourning over the flowing waters of Hsiang.

The purple rings which Tsui Chi describes, viewed scientifically, are probably the zoned, cloud-shaped patterns produced by certain fungi on many species of bamboo in China and Japan. A Japanese botanist notes that the culm of Ruihantiku (tear-stained bamboo) has beautiful figures composed by an ascomycetous fungus and that these figures are quite similar to those of the Chinese Hsiang-nü-chu, which is world renowned for the beauty of its culm figures. The fungus described was found on specimens of a bamboo known by the scientific name *Semi-arundinaria fastuosa* and by the popular name Narihira Beau Brummel because of its esthetic appeal as an ornamental plant.

Bamboos, once they are well established, are probably the fastest growing of the higher plants. In Ceylon, *Dendrocalamus giganteus* has been observed to grow sixteen inches in a day. The timber bamboo, *Phyllostachys bambusoides,* reaches its full height of about seventy feet in six to eight weeks. Some bamboos attain a height of over a hundred feet in two or three months, growing two, three, or even more feet in twenty-four hours.

When bamboo stems sprout they may be solid or hollow, depending on the species, and when they are several inches high they have attained their full diameter. Solid shoots become hollow as they grow. Silicic hardening of the culms begins as soon as the tissues at each level have ceased elongation, and about three years are required to complete it. The outer layer of the culms is heavily overlaid with a waxy covering, or cuticle, which prevents loss of water. In addition it is strengthened and protected by incrustations of silica on the outer wall and infiltration of this element into the wall. This hard covering makes bamboo culms still more impervious to moisture, more durable than ordinary wood of the same weight, and as much as ten times as resistant to tearing. Some bamboos have such heavy deposits of silica on the outside of their culms that they can be used as whetstones.

During the growth of the culms the internodes of some species are partly filled with water containing silica in solution. As the foliage develops the water is transpired, in some species leaving small masses of a solid, or soft, milk-white residue called *tabasheer* or *tabishir*. This strange substance has been found to be a hydrous silica, practically identical with the hydropane variety of mineral opal. Tabasheer has strange optical qualities in that its refractive power is much lower than that of water—being intermediate between air and water. Its physical qualities are uniform throughout and it is both opalescent and phosphorescent. Remarkably porous, with an absorptive power greater than any of the minerals, tabasheer will absorb its own weight in water. Yet the pores are so fine that they cannot be seen under an ordinary microscope. When saturated, tabasheer is completely translucent. Some identify this strange by-product of the bamboos as the gem *oculus mundi,* eye of the world, described by gem writers of the sixteenth, seventeenth, and eighteenth centuries. Tabasheer was long valued as a medicine in the East, but modern science says it has no medicinal properties.

Unlike most grasses of the temperate zone, but in common with many tropical grasses, the bamboos put out branches at their upper nodes when they reach their full height. These branches are always two-ranked and alternate like the leaves. In some species the branches are long and spreading, in others drooping and intricately ramified. Sometimes the branches produce tough hooked spines. The blades of the leaves, often graceful and slender, are usually only a few inches long, but may reach a length of more than a foot and a breadth of two inches in *Sasa palmata.* The upper end is tapered to a slender point; the base is gently rounded.

These blades differ from those of other grasses by being jointed at the base and attached to the long sheath by a slender stalk. The spikelets may have one, a few, or many flowers, arranged in a variety of ways in racemes and panicles.

The beauty of the bamboos can be realized fully only by those who have seen them growing. With their soaring lacquer-smooth resilient stems, branching toward the top and flaunting delicate narrow leaves, they bend and rustle in the breeze and every shadow pattern is full of airy grace. Songbirds love the bamboo thickets and add their liquid notes to the music of the whispering leaves. In China and Japan the artist's brush never tires of painting clumps and sprays of bamboo. And although the bamboos grow wild in multiple variety, the painstaking oriental gardener plants them with care and lavishes upon them the most loving attention. The Chinese have many treatises on bamboo culture, based on centuries of experience. These tell how and when to plant the different species, the best types of soil for bringing them to perfection, the best kind of water for their proper growth, and how to train the growing stems into various desired shapes.

Bamboos give a dainty accent to oriental gardens and are making themselves increasingly at home in those of the Western World, but a native forest of bamboos—especially of the giants—is awesome and strange. Even seasoned travelers feel transported to a different dimension when standing in a grove of these weirdly beautiful, outsized grasses.

When plant explorer David Fairchild revisited in Ceylon a clump of the great Burmese bamboo, *Dendrocalamus giganteus,* he felt again his original awe as he looked up at the Gargantuan culms.

"You do not appreciate its remarkable character," he wrote in *Exploring for Plants,* "until you are standing with one hand on a hollow stem almost a foot through and holding in the other one of the great stem sheaths as large as a drainboard and as thick as a piece of heavy cardboard. You look up a hundred and twenty feet along the hollow stem you have your hand on, and see no sign of a branch for seventy-five feet, just the smooth green stem that is jointed, like a grass, all the way up to the slender leafy tip waving in the breeze. You feel like a Lilliputian in a bunch of meadow grass."

Writing of the giant American bamboo, the spiny *Guadua* of Colombia and Ecuador, a scientist of the nineteenth century, Dr. G. L. Hartwig, penned this description: "In New Granada and Quito the *Guadua* . . .

ranks next to the sugarcane and maize as the plant most indispensable to man. It forms dense jungles, not only in the lower regions of the country but in the valleys of the Andes, five thousand feet above the level of the sea. The culms attain a thickness of six inches, the single joints are twenty inches long, and the leaves are of indescribable beauty. A whole

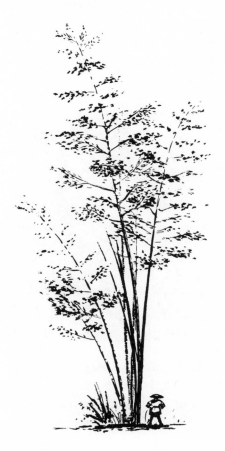

hut can be built and thatched with the *Guadua,* while the single joints are extensively used as water vessels and drinking cups."

Turning his attention to the rich variety of the bamboos of India, he tells how they grow along the banks of lakes and rivers, in low marshy grounds, as well as in elevated mountain regions where "they chiefly form the impenetrable forests, the seat of the tiger and python."

"Sometimes," he wrote, "a hundred culms spring from a single root, not seldom as thick as a man, and towering to a height of eighty to a hundred feet. Fancy the grace of our meadow grasses, united with the lordly growth of the Italian poplar, and you will have a faint idea of the beauty of a clump of bamboos."

So numerous and varied are the uses of bamboo that no list could hope to be complete. This is an all-purpose grass, nor do its thousand and one uses depend upon chemical processing. In China, India, Japan and other islands of the East, and parts of South America, it offers a prefinished construction and handicraft material, both beautiful and durable, that is adaptable to a myriad of uses. It also provides food.

In former days it supplied oriental armies with battle weapons—bows, arrows, lances, sharp-pointed barricades, scaling ladders—and provided material for houses, furniture, kitchen utensils, farming tools, fishing gear, rafts, boats, and bridges. A bucket or cup, needing only a handle, could be made in a few minutes from a section of stem, the stout plate at the joint forming the base. Lashed stems made a sturdy raft. Strong fibers, twisted together, provided rope and thin strips could be woven into baskets. The tough silica-hardened cuticle provided knives and even sharpeners. All of these uses continue to the present day.

Fire in a bamboo forest heats the air contained in the internodes and makes them burst with a report almost like the roar of cannon. Early Chinese found that the exploding bamboos were good for chasing away wild animals and for routing the ghosts and goblins that haunt primitive people. It was their custom to build night fires near bamboo groves so that the heated stems might explode and frighten off such malevolent spirits. The botanist Hui-lin Li says firecrackers, used to chase bad luck, were developed from this practice as the name *pao chu,* or cracking bamboo, clearly indicates. When they had invented gunpowder the Chinese stuffed it into bamboo tubes and thus had a noise maker and devil chaser that could be carried conveniently anywhere for use as indicated. Eventually paper wrappings were substituted for the bamboo tubes and the firecracker was born.

Dr. Li adds that Chinese culture is deeply indebted to the versatile bamboo. In a fascinating article written for the *Journal of the New York Botanical Garden* he maintains that music, law, and the calendar in China—all expressions of rhythm in the view of ancient sages—owe their origin to the manipulation of bamboo. It is recorded, he says, that when Ling Lun was instructed by the first emperor to found the art of music, he used twelve bamboo tubes of different lengths to determine the twelve notes, or *lu.* The earliest musical instruments of China were made of bamboo and of these the flute survives, its liquid notes sounding from China to Ceylon in music sad but strangely sweet. Another ancient musical instrument was the *cheng* or *sheng,* a mouth organ with a crook mouthpiece. Thirteen of the tubes had free reeds with holes just above the point where they entered the reservoir, and sound was produced only when the holes were covered. This principle of the free reed is employed in the grand organs of today.

Music was regarded by the ancient Chinese as a fundamental prerequisite of government, continues Dr. Li, and that law has come from music is evident because it has the same character as the musical note, *lu*. Similarly, the Chinese lunar calendar owed its development to a certain extent to the use of bamboo tubes. In order to determine the solar periods, so vital to agriculture in ancient times, "the ash of certain grasses was placed in a number of bamboo tubes which represented the different solar dates. When the proper time arrived the ash was said to fly out from one of the tubes, and the phenomenon determined the exact time of the solar year. If the ash really behaved thus because of a change in the weather or in atmospheric pressure, this early bamboo instrument might be called a crude barometer. By this strange token the ancient Chinese was expected to plant his crops." Dr. Li continues: "Moreover the record of date, and later also the year, month and hour, was made by the *kan-chih* or stem-branch system. There are ten *kan* and twelve *chih,* which are arranged to give sixty combinations. The stem and branch were developed out of that of the trees and although there was no record pointing particularly toward bamboo, nevertheless it is in this plant that the main stem and side branches are most readily recognizable.

"Bamboo is responsible for the beginnings of mathematics. The earliest form of arithmetic was calculating by means of bamboo billets *ch'ou*. They were also used for computing numbers as counters in archery and other games. Bamboo is also responsible for providing numerous amusements for the Chinese people. Many of these have gradually become means of gambling. The character for gambling, *pe,* was originally written with the sign of bamboo at its top, in recognition of its relation to bamboo. The first material for making chessmen, cards, dice, and many other games was bamboo.

"The unit of measurement, the Chinese foot *ch'ih* was derived from bamboo blocks for written records, as the latter were frequently known as *chi'ih chieh* or *chi tu*. The length of the block equaled one *ch'ih,* and it was also the average length between the nodes of the bamboo culms. The block had to be made from the internodal part to avoid the joints and it eventually led to its use as a unit of measurement. Up to the present, bamboo strips are still used throughout the Orient as rulers."

Bamboo was one of the first sources of paper, an invention of the Chinese some two thousand years ago. (Papyrus, used by the Egyptians,

was made by pasting strips of reed together and was not real paper.)
But before paper was made bamboo was used in China for keeping records. Hui-Lin Li believes the earliest practice was to carve
records on living bamboo culms. Growth of the bamboo, he thinks,
altered the characters and influenced later forms. The first books in
China consisted of records cut on bamboo blocks which were then
fastened together. Silk and linen cloth superseded the blocks and was
used until paper took the place of both. Dr. Li thinks that paper may
have been suggested by the paperlike inner layer of the bamboo culm
which is often used to seal the second hole of the flute. The inner layers
of the culms were pulped by hand to make the earliest bamboo paper.

Bamboo is no less important in the Orient today than in ancient times.
In South China, Japan, and Java many houses are built almost entirely
of bamboo. Stout culms provide ready-made posts, slender stems make
the rafters, large bamboos the floor joists, and split culms the floorboards.
Roof, walls, shutters, and windowframes are fashioned of strips and
culms, and sometime bamboo leaves are used to thatch the roof. Mats
of woven bamboo, called *biliks,* are used in Java for the outside walls
of houses. Two biliks, with air space between are used for each side.
They are made to measure and are often seen being carried through the
streets to location; doors and windows are cut in them as fancy dictates
after they have been secured in place. Such walls are good looking and
airy, yet provide snug protection against inclement weather even during
heavy tropical rains. Very attractive bamboo fences may encircle the
grounds of the house and inside may be found woven bamboo furniture,
curtains, mats, bedding, screens, bird cages, chop sticks and other utensils, boxes, trays, baskets, and ornaments.

Cables, masts, and sails of Chinese junks are made of bamboo. Sometimes three or more stems are built up and joined to make quite large
masts. Very thin strips, made by splitting the whole length of a culm,
are twisted into stout ropes for nautical uses.

Other articles which the Oriental fashions of bamboo include pens,
holders for pens and pencils, paper knives, smoking pipes, sedan chairs,
fishing poles, utensils for collecting and raising fish, snares for tigers,
beautiful baskets, musical instruments, umbrellas, canes, life preservers,
and the paraphernalia used in rearing silkworms. (Incidentally, it was
a bamboo joint that concealed the silkworms which were smuggled out

of China to Constantinople during the reign of Justinian. Up to that time the manufacture of silk had been a carefully guarded secret.) Water pipes are made of bamboo stems by boring out the septa and joining the stems together lengthwise. These are used to carry water to gardens, pools, and reservoirs. And, of very great modern importance, the quick growing bamboos provide the Orient with her vast paper requirements.

Food also is provided by the bamboos. The shoots of all known species of *Phyllostachys* are edible, the most esteemed being *P. dulcis* and *P. viridis*. These are hilled and grown like asparagus. They are served like asparagus too, or in combination with other foods. Sometimes they are candied or pickled. The grain of the bamboos is good to eat, but since seeding is irregular it cannot be depended upon as a staple food source. A Chinese proverb says that the bamboos produce seeds most abundantly when the rice crop fails. While this may or may not be completely accurate, it is probably true that the bamboos, with their periodic lavish crops of grain, have helped save the Chinese people many times during rice famines. The seeds are also used for making beer and candy. In India a special confection is made by mixing equal parts of seeds and honey, stuffing this into a bamboo tube, and roasting it, covered with clay, in a fire. In some bamboos the seed is a nut. *Melocanna bambusoides* produces a fruit about the size of an apple which is baked and eaten.

Though but two genera of bamboo are native to the United States, many Chinese and Japanese varieties have been introduced and are making themselves very much at home in American gardens. There are groves of oriental bamboos more than fifty years old in Louisiana, Georgia, and California, whose origin is more or less of a mystery. In recent years many introductions have been made by the United States Department of Agriculture. We of the West have been inclined to think of the bamboos as exotic ornamental plants or as a quaint handicraft material not adapted to our machine age. This is quite definitely not the case.

At the turn of the century, when Thomas Edison was experimenting with incandescent electric lamps, he found that a carbonized filament of a certain species of bamboo, a fine wire-like sliver from an internode, provided the best light-giving element. Dr. Floyd A. McClure, outstanding American authority on the bamboos, believes that in his early experiments Edison used fibers from the species *Chusquea pittieri* that grows wild in the high mountain jungles of Panama. Bamboo filament lamps were still in use as late as 1910 and at about this time some of the phonograph-needle manufacturers began to use bamboo.

These uses surely pointed to a future for bamboo in the rapidly advancing scientific age. Indeed the alert eyes of botanists had long been focused on the bamboos. As the years passed, and stand after stand of American softwoods yielded to the demands of the paper and rayon industries, scientists visualized in these fast-growing grasses a possible source of cellulose to meet the increasing demands of industry.

American forests were being depleted to fill the nation's need for pulp and fiber, and conservationists were alarmed. A reforestation project was undertaken, but in spite of extensive plantings wood consumption still outran forest growth. Furthermore, about eighteen years were required to develop a southern pine stand to the point of thinning and about thirty for it to reach maturity.

Experimentation began with many species of bamboo. In contrast to forest trees which grow so slowly, the shoots of well established plants of some of the bamboos may reach a height of seventy feet in two months or less. Under favorable conditions a plantation could be firmly established in ten years and after that could be cut repeatedly for years on a three- to five-year cycle. Furthermore there was no bark to be peeled from the stems and more cellulose was produced. Bamboo pulp produced paper of standard or superior quality and could be used for fine rayons. And it has been estimated that a stand of bamboo may produce six times as much cellulose an acre as southern pine, the main source of pulp in the United States. The genus *Phyllostachys* is the main source of paper pulp and other raw materials in China and about thirty-five species and horticultural varieties of these bamboos have been introduced and grown in this country. The timber bamboo, *Phyllostachys bambusoides,* produces eight to nine tons of pulp an acre at the Plant Introduction Station in Savannah, Georgia.

Today, in Savannah, high-grade paper and newsprint are being machine-made from bamboo on an experimental basis. But in the Orient, where hand-dipped bamboo pulp kept China and other nations supplied with paper for centuries, born craftsmen have turned to labor-saving machines. In China, India, Japan, Thailand, and Burma modern paper mills are humming and machine-made bamboo paper is coming from the rollers in an endless stream. Brazil and France also are producing machine-made paper from bamboo culms. In India, where more than a quarter of a million tons of bamboo paper are made each year, the Forest Research Institute at Dehra Dun acknowledges in a gracious way the importance of these grasses by publishing its annual report on bamboo paper.

Bamboos planted in the expanses of undeveloped land in our southern states could make a great contribution toward saving our forests from overcutting by supplying cellulose for both paper and rayon. Certain species of bamboo are very highly adapted to the making of rayon and attention is being given them in both North and South America. But in India the experimental phase has passed. A company in Travancore is producing excellent bamboo rayon on a commercial scale.

Experts on bamboo believe that it might be possible to build up existing stands of our native bamboos to provide a continuing source of cellulose for paper, rayon, and other products—a source to take the pressure off the forests. Constant experimentation with imported species also points the way to growing valuable exotic bamboos on land that is now unproductive.

Farms already provided with bamboo groves are harvesting home-grown bamboo shoots for the table, stakes for plants, poles for harvesting pecans and gathering Spanish moss, with side profits from seasoned culms sold for rug poles, boat masts, flagstaffs, fishing rods, decorative fences, curtains, screens, furniture and radio antennae poles.

In the Orient, houses, theaters, and bridges are built of bamboo and this has led to thoroughgoing tests of its structural uses in this country. Dr. Fairchild saw in Java a long suspension bridge spanning a mountain torrent like a giant cobweb. It was built entirely of bamboo culms, tied together, except for the four corner posts which were of heavy timber. Not a nail or screw was visible. The bridge demonstrated the advantages and disadvantages of bamboo as a construction material. For pulling strains it is the equal, weight for weight, of steel, but it lacks rigidity—hence the timber posts. Though not new, the bridge at that time (around 1930) showed no sign of deterioration except in the tying materials. Even so, the decay was nothing compared to the rusting that goes on unnoticed in a steel bridge unless it is carefully painted.

Exhaustive tests of bamboo culms of different varieties, seasoned and unseasoned, treated and untreated, have been made under the direction of H. E. Glenn, at the Engineering Experiment Station of Clemson College, South Carolina. These tests gave the average maximum tensile strength of all species and varieties as about 37,000 pounds a square inch in the internodes and about 32,500 pounds a square inch in the nodes. Experiments were then made in the use of bamboo as reinforcement for cement. Long slender culms were laid longitudinally in the cement to reinforce beams, girders, and slabs in experimental buildings. The bamboo reinforced units were found in tests to be able to stand a load four or five times greater than units of the same dimensions that had no reinforcement. The prefabrication of bamboo strengthened cement building units has been proved to be entirely feasible.

Bamboo table mats, curtains, and furniture are especially attractive in modern-type houses and are now seen in department stores everywhere. Experiment is needed for the furniture because the culms of these giant, silica-toughened grasses split easily and require special carpentry skills. In some parts of the Orient techniques have been developed which do not call for nails. Bamboo structures in Java, for instance, are tied together with strips of tali bamboo, and bamboo brackets figure cleverly as reinforcements at angles. To make a floorboard from a large culm two men work together, starting at opposite ends. With short heavy knives they crack the joints nearest them in about a dozen evenly spaced places, turning the culm as they proceed. The second, third, and succeeding joints are cracked until the two men meet in the middle. Then each retreats to his own end of the hollow "log." With a sharp stroke of the knives the stem is cut completely through. It is then thrown open so that it lies flat on the ground and the three-cornered broken partitions, cracked in the first operation, are shaved off. The split culm is spread out and a smooth, polished, resilient floorboard—consisting of strips held together by their own fibers—is ready to be fastened into place. Experts on bamboo agree that we must study the clever methods that oriental peoples have developed of fastening, nailing, splitting, and perforating bamboo before we can excel in making furniture. Western devices, however, have been perfected to join culms and these include threaded aluminum plugs, thinly coated with plastic adhesive, which are welded electronically in a precisely reamed bamboo. Another device is a hook and nut union. These can be used in making furniture, ladders, and sporting equipment.

As Dr. McClure says, "the promise of bamboo is great." Broadened knowledge of the giant grasses and more widespread use in the West seem probable. And, in our efforts to conserve the forests—sorely needed for erosion and flood control, the protection of the underground water supply, and for building material—the bamboos may in the future play a heroic role indeed.

The Grass
That Gives Us Sugar

(Saccharum officinarum)

*When shall we have any good sugar come
over? The wars in Barbary make sugar
at such an excessive rate, you pay sweetly
now, I warrant, sir, do you not?*

Thomas Dekker

Many hundreds of years ago, in the lush tropics of the mysterious East, a pioneer plant explorer found a curious kind of tall grass with knotted juicy stems that were sweet to the taste like honey. That grass was sugarcane, source of the world's first manufactured sugar and its most important source today.

Two-thirds of the world's annual production of fifty million tons of sugar is derived from this giant perennial grass that grows only in tropical or near-tropical regions—in moist rich earth, preferably near the sea. Sugarcane has been prized highly since the most ancient times and cultivated for centuries.

Almost all green plants make sugar, some half-dozen on a commercial scale, but none so efficiently as sugarcane. About eighty per cent of the weight of its stalks is juice, ready for the first step in processing. Sugar is an exclusive product of the plant world. Two simple materials go into it, carbon dioxide and water, yet man cannot duplicate the process of photosynthesis by which it is manufactured in plants. Photosynthesis produces sugar in plants by combining carbon dioxide, absorbed by the leaves from the air, with water from the soil by the action of sunlight in the presence of the green coloring matter called chlorophyll. Oxygen is released by the plants in exchange for the carbon dioxide, and we in turn breathe the oxygen and give off carbon dioxide, thus completing the cycle. Sugar has been called the foundation of all life because all of

111

our foods—oils, fats, starches, and proteins—are derived from it directly or indirectly, while its by-product, oxygen, is the life-sustaining constituent of the air we breathe.

There are many varieties of sugarcane but none hardy enough to grow in cold climates. Tropical India for years led the world in sugar production but lost first place when Pakistan became a separate country. Today Cuba leads, with India second. Brazil, Australia, the Philippine Islands, Mexico, Hawaii, Pakistan, the Dominican Republic, and Taiwan follow in that order. Some sugarcane is grown in the United States, mainly in Louisiana and Florida, but not nearly enough to meet our requirements. Thus it is that most of the sugar we use comes to us from distant lands, and this is true also of the British Isles and the countries of Europe. Sugar has followed the world's sea routes to its markets ever since it was introduced in the West. When wars disrupt shipping it is one of the first shortages felt.

Those fearless sea rovers, the Phoenicians, who steered their ships by the North Star as early as 1500 B.C., probably introduced sugar to world trade. They are said to have taken it as an eastern curiosity to Europe and the British Isles in the immemorial past. But knowledge of the sugar plant of the Orient seems to have been lost to the Western World during the dark ages that followed the fall of the Roman Empire.

No one can say with certainty where sugarcane first grew or how long it has been known and cultivated. The Old Testament speaks of "sweet cane from a far country," but Biblical authorities are pretty well agreed that the reference applies to a sweet-smelling reed found in North Africa. In the records of Nearchus, a Greek admiral who helped Alexander the Great explore the Indus River in 325 B.C., there is a note of the discovery of "honey-bearing reeds." Several centuries later the Greek physician, Dioscorides, wrote during the reign of Nero that "there is a sort of hard honey, which is called saccharum (sugar) found upon the canes in India. It is grainy like salt and brittle between the teeth withal."

Many botanists believe that the native home of sugarcane was India, with a possible range in primitive times through Cochin China and the Malay Archipelago. Other eminent authorities believe that sugarcane originated in the Pacific Islands and was transported later to China and India.

Nor is it certain whether farmers of India or China were the first to cultivate it. One writer, George Richardson Porter, says: "The strongest proofs, carefully collected from the authorities of ancient and modern times, lead to the conclusion that China was the first country in which sugarcane was cultivated and its produce manufactured." Another, Prinsen Geerligs, says with equal conviction that "no real preparation is recorded before about A.D. 600, at which time a Chinese emperor sent a man to learn the art of sugar making in India." Whichever is right it is obvious that sugarcane was known throughout the Orient at a very early time and that sugar of some sort was made. In the Ganges area of India the art of boiling sugar was early understood and historians believe that the technique was carried to China in the first half of the seventh century. The art of refining it could not have been known then, for the Chinese learned it only during the Mongol period from Egyptian visitors. In the Middle Ages the best sugar came from Egypt and, up to recent times, coarse sugar was called Chinese in India, while fine sugar was known as Cairene or Egyptian.

The cultivation of sugarcane spread from China to Siam, Ceylon, Japan, and other islands. Westward it reached Persia and at Gunde-Shapur in this region, according to an ancient Armenian geography, "sugar was prepared with art" at about the time of the Arab conquest, and its manufacture was carried out on a large scale at Shuster, Sus, and Askar Mokram throughout the Middle Ages. The eleventh century writer Tha'alibi says Askar Mokram had no peer for the quality and amount of its sugar. The city paid in annual tribute to the sultan alone fifty thousand pounds. The Arabs carried sugar far and wide from these ancient locations and it has been conjectured that the art of refining it may have been developed by their famous physicians, who valued it highly as a medicine. (In European languages the word "sugar" comes by way of the Arabic tongue from the Persian *shakar*.) By A.D. 800 the Arabs had taken sugar with them to Morocco, Sicily, and southern Spain and were growing cane in those areas.

To most of Europe sugar was unknown until the Crusades brought East and West into violent contact. From the Moslems the European invaders learned of silks, spices, sugar, and other luxuries and their glowing accounts created a demand for these exotic products. A brisk trade developed between Europe and the East. Through the ports of Venice and Genoa the rich traffic flowed, making those cities wealthy and powerful. And the cultivation of sugarcane now was extended to Rhodes, Malta, and the sultry plains at the foot of Mount Etna in Italy. One of the earliest references to sugar in England is the record of the shipment of 100,000 pounds to London in 1319 by the Venetian merchant Tomasso Loredano in exchange for wool.

At this time an age of great restlessness was dawning in the Western World—an urge to create and to explore. New trade routes were being sought to the fabulous East for exploration and commerce. In the last half of the thirteenth century the Polos walked from Italy to China, passing through many strange and mysterious lands, including the sugar

growing provinces of Bengal, and visiting cities such as Kin-sai and Un-guen. Of Un-guen, "remarkable for its manufacture of sugar," Marco Polo wrote: "Previously to its being brought under the dominion of the Great Khan, the natives were unacquainted with the art of manufacturing fine sugar, and boiled it in such an imperfect manner that when left to cool it remained in the state of a dark brown paste. But at the time this city became subject to his Majesty's government there happened to be at the court some persons from Babylon [Persians?] who were skilled in the process and who, being sent thither, instructed the inhabitants in the mode of refining the sugar by means of the ashes of certain woods."

Walking to the Far East was scarcely practical for trading purposes and at the time no one believed Marco Polo's wonderful stories. The search continued for a route by water.

In 1420, Dom Enrique of Portugal, called Prince Henry the Navigator, stood on a lonely bluff at Sagres and looked southwest over the Atlantic Sea of Darkness. One of the first soldiers of his age, he had renounced his command and taken up his abode at this lonely and desolate post to plan the exploration of unknown seas to the west and south. West of Africa lay a world of storms. He planned to overcome it—to get around the continent to the south and sail to India, China, and the islands beyond. Only a genius and a very determined man could have withstood the years that followed. Prince Henry studied navigation, made maps, and established an observatory, the first in Portugal. Days and often nights were spent in hard work. His household evolved into a rigorously disciplined school of navigation, attracting venturesome young nobles of his country. For twelve years Dom Enrique sent out his caravels, two or three each year, only to meet failure. Finally, in 1453, Gil Eannes safely doubled Cape Bojador—rockbound, shrouded in mists, and skirted by hazardous, far-reaching shallows. Bojador had long been the southern limit of navigation and its shore was studded with the bleaching timbers of dead ships. Henry the Navigator now pushed courageously farther south.

The fall of Constantinople to the Turks in 1453 made Henry's work of great importance, for the Turks were exacting high tribute from passing caravans. The discovery of new sea routes was almost imperative if trade were to continue.

Dom Enrique paved the way for explorers like Diogo Cam, Vasco da Gama, Columbus, Balboa, and Magellan. He also took sugar a step farther. From Cyprus and Sicily he sent cane for planting to the sunny island of Madeira. From Madeira it was taken to the Canary Islands in 1503. Columbus took cuttings of sugarcane to the New World on his second voyage and told, in his letters, how he planted them and how luxuriously they grew. According to Washington Irving's biography, Columbus, to win the confidence of the Indians whom he persuaded to visit aboard his ship "gave them beads, hawks' bells and sugar and sent them highly gratified on shore." Early in the sixteenth century sugarcane reached Brazil and Haiti; then it traveled to Mexico, Cuba, Guadeloupe,

Martinique, and Bourbon (Réunion). From Brazil, introduced there by the Portuguese, it was taken to the Barbados in 1614 and from there it was distributed throughout the West Indies.

From the "sugar islands" of the Caribbean the crude product of that day, made in ox-driven mills, made the long journey to Spain in stately galleons. Often the ships were seized and plundered by pirates, who valued sugar almost as much as gold. By 1600 sugar production had hit its stride. It has been described as the greatest industry in the world at that time.

In spite of the many ramifications of sugarcane culture, sugar was in comparatively limited supply and a minor article of trade until it reached tropical America. Captain Cook discovered a new and superior variety in Tahiti and sugar plantations flourished as it was distributed quickly to sugar-growing areas. But ancient transportation methods, crude refining processes, and the lack of an efficient distribution system kept the price high. An old print featuring a price list of different foods itemizes sugar as selling for the equivalent of $2.75 a pound in London in 1742. The vogue for tea and coffee is said to have given the industry its first great impetus.

And now let us end our historical survey and look closely at this fabulous grass that produces most of the sugar used in the world's cuisine. Sugarcane resembles corn and sorghum in its habit of growth. The solid juicy stems grow in clumps from a stout rhizome and usually attain a height of ten to twenty feet, though canes forty-two feet tall have been measured. The canes vary in diameter from one-half inch to three inches. The smallest are seldom grown and the largest, elephant cane, a native of Cochin China, is grown only as an ornamental plant. The internodes of the stalk are four to six inches long near the base. They become longer toward the top where they end in a very long section called the arrow, which supports the great panicle of flowers. Tasseling arrows make a pretty picture but, nearly always, the cane is cut before flowering time. Arrowing is considered a detriment to the yield, so much so that in Cuba an old Spanish proverb says that arrowing cane means a ruined planter.

Sugarcane stalks of different varieties, when they are fully matured, resemble an assortment of giant candy sticks. Though they are golden green at first they gradually assume distinctive colors. Many are vividly striped or splotched with contrasting hues. Dark purple, violet, and red violet culms are fairly common. Others are ruby red, yellow, pale bluish green, rose, pink, white, pinkish orange, and almost black. A pale green variety has dark red broken stripes. A red violet is striped with pinky violet and a dark purple has bold orange stripes. Another, olive green, is blotched with red violet, and a muddy yellow or green cane has dark red stripes, evenly spaced. Many striped canes, when planted, produce plants with stems of either of the two colors as well as striped. Sometimes such color variations are seen in stems sprouting from the same bud.

The leaf blades of sugarcane spring from a sheath that may be as long as twelve inches. The sheath surrounds the stalk completely just above the node, then gradually recedes from it. The blades are from three to four feet long and two or three inches wide at the base, gradually tapering to a point. Their edges are delicately serrated. In some of the purple varieties the leaf sheath, the lower sides of the leaves, even the entire leaf, may also be purple. Some are white, or variegated green and white, but most often the leaves are in some shade of green. The midrib is usually white, although sometimes it has a red or purple tinge. In many varieties of sugar cane, hairs (*setae*) are found at the base of the leaf blade and these can inflict painful skin punctures.

At each node of the stalk, just above the leaf, there is a dormant eye, or bud, like that of a potato. About the size of a pea, the eye may be triangular, round, or oval. Around the node is also a ring of very tiny whitish dots. The eye is the embryo of a new plant and the white dots are the beginnings of roots which will nourish and support the baby plant in the earth. These eyes are very important in sugarcane culture.

From eight to fifteen months are required for sugarcane to mature. The flowers are borne on silky soft spikelets arranged on a large graceful panicle and may be silvery white, white-tinted lilac, or purple. They appear at a definite time of year, which varies in different regions, and if the cane has not matured to the flowering stage at blossom time no flowers will appear until the following year. Some canes never bloom at all and rarely do the flowers produce fertile seeds. Indeed it was believed until 1885 that none of the seeds would grow. The seeds, when they do appear, are very tiny. Magnified they are seen to resemble grains of wheat, but about a hundred would be required to equal the weight of a single wheat kernel. Sugarcane has all but lost its ability to produce fertile seeds because it has been grown from cuttings for many centuries.

Modern practice is to cut for planting, pieces twelve to twenty-four inches long from the upper end of the stalks. Each piece will contain three nodes with their dormant buds, or eyes. In a deep-plowed fertile field the stalks are placed end to end in shallow furrows four to six feet

apart and covered with two to four inches of soil. The planting can be done at any time of the year when soil, temperature, and moisture are favorable. If conditions are good the eyes sprout within a few days, producing a new cane that emerges as a single leaf rolled and tapered to a sharp point. The leaf soon yields to a bud and the little plant shoots up, developing within a few weeks nodes, internodes, and sword-shaped arching leaves. As the cane grows the bottom leaves dry up and fall, leaving the lower stalks bare while the upper part continues green and growing until it is mature or cold weather arrests its growth.

Cane fields are cultivated principally to control weeds. Heavy applications of fertilizer are often made because sugarcane requires ample nourishment. It also needs a great deal of water while it is growing and when rainfall is insufficient the fields may be irrigated. The harvest takes place from eight to thirty months after planting, depending upon conditions, and at that time the field consists of many primary stalks and side-branching tillers. In the sugar growing areas of the United States, in Hawaii, and Australia the cane is planted and harvested mechanically, but on most of the world's sugar plantations it is hand cut close to the ground with large steel knives, or machêtes. Sometimes the knife has a hook on the back of the blade which is used to strip off the leaves. In Hawaii the fields are often fired to burn off the leaves before harvesting the canes.

After the cane is cut at its base, the top is lopped of at the last matured joint and the leaves are removed. The canes are left in windrows to be loaded and transported by truck, cart, or railway cars to the nearest raw sugar factory. Sometimes, when plantations are situated on mountain slopes, the canes are floated down through a series of flumes made by diverting a river through the fields at a high altitude. The flumes converge at the sugar factory below and deliver the canes at the door of the crushing plant. Speed is necessary because unless the

canes are ground within twenty-four to forty-eight hours after cutting there is a loss in sugar recovery.

The first growth of a planting is called plant cane. Thereafter the root sends up canes called ratoons which may be cut as a crop, usually every twelve months, for two or three years. But in Cuba, on virgin soil, a planting may produce a crop for ten or fifteen years.

Sugar yields vary according to the fertility of the soil, the amount of moisture, and weather conditions. Cold weather arrests the growth of the canes. In the richest sugarcane producing areas more than half a ton of sugar an acre is produced each month during the harvesting period.

For many years sugarcane was unknown in a wild state and was believed to exist only in cultivated forms that were unable to perpetuate themselves. But *Saccharum robustum,* a wild species, has been found distributed widely in New Guinea, and another relative, the slender *S. spontaneum,* has been found growing throughout India, Malaya, the Philippines, and the East Indian islands. Though the wild species resemble closely some of the cultivated canes, they are pithy and contain little sugar. Botanists attribute the superior sugarcanes grown today to chance mutation or the accidental crossing of wild species, followed by long-continued selective planting and cultivation. The juicy types grown today cannot survive in a wild state. But wild canes in recent years have played important roles in the development of new varieties, superior to the old in sugar content and in their ability to resist diseases.

Since sugarcane had been grown from cuttings for so many centuries no one even thought of planting seeds until the end of the nineteenth century. In 1858 a planter in Barbados, J. W. Parris, had found seedling canes growing around the edges of a flowering field and coaxed them to maturity, but little attention was paid to the feat. Some thirty years later an English chemist in Barbados and a Dutch botanist in the mountains of Java independently reported success in growing seedlings. The Englishman, J. B. Harrison, had found strange grasslike plants in a sugarcane field. He thought they might be seedlings and, though everyone told him they were field grass, he proved his theory. In Java the Dutchman, F. Saltwedel, went a little further. He pollinated the flowers of two wild canes, the glagah (*Saccharum spontaneum*) and the glonggong (*S. saltwedeli*), just to see what would happen when he planted their seeds.

The work of these pioneers stimulated widespread interest in the possibility of producing crosses that could resist some of the diseases that ravage sugarcane fields at different times and in various places. Sugarcane breeding soon became an important function of experiment stations throughout the tropical growing regions. New varieties were soon being produced which doubled the yield of sugar yet shared with their wild sisters the ability to resist disease. These complex hybrids combine the desirable qualities of many parent plants. Since they are propagated by means of cuttings, the fact that hybrids do not always breed true does not have to be considered.

Production of the sparkling white cane sugar that we take for granted today is a major industry, highly mechanized and based upon the most painstaking research in field and laboratory. Comparatively speaking, white granulated sugar is new. Up to the end of the eighteenth century the manufacturing process was crude and so was the product. Mills powered by wind, water, or oxen were used to crush the stalks and extract the juice. The purifying agents employed were lime, clay, or ashes. Evaporation took place in open iron or copper pots placed directly over a fire, and "refining" was accomplished by melting, boiling, and recrystallizing the sugar sirup. Sometimes the damp, yellowish mass was molded into cone-shaped loaves of various sizes, an innovation of a fifteenth-century Venetian. The peaked sugar loaf gave its name to innumerable mountains before vanishing from the general scene toward the end of the nineteenth century. In the United States it was produced quite generally by refineries as late as 1875 and was discontinued only after the invention of the "granulator," an atmospheric rotary drier. Many older people of the last generation remembered the conical sugar loaves, always wrapped in blue paper. Dr. George P. Meade, of New Orleans, tells us he saw two-pound loaves of the conical shape being produced in Belgium as late as 1949 for export to Persia and Arabia.

The first granulated sugar made in the United States was produced on a very small scale by Antonio Mendez in 1792. Several years later Etienne de Boré succeeded in growing the first successful sugar crop in the United States and began to produce sugar on a commercial scale. Both of these men owned plantations in Louisiana, within the present limits of New Orleans. De Boré's success in growing sugarcane established the sugar industry in Louisiana. He followed methods already practiced in the West Indies and was not, as legend contends, the first person to make granulated sugar. The sugar he made was very coarse, produced by draining the molasses from the sugar crystals. It was Norbert Rillieux, inventor of the multiple effect evaporator in 1845, who brought Louisiana fame in the world sugar industry. Within fifteen years use of the evaporator had become world-wide.

Two main steps are involved in producing the pure white crystalline sugar we use today: recovery of the raw sugar from the cane and its refining. The cane is taken quickly from the fields to a raw sugar mill or "central." If it travels by rail it goes in freight cars with sides that are hinged at the top, which can be switched onto tilting tables. The cane, dumped from the cars, slides from the tables onto conveyors that lead directly to the crushing rolls. Here, between pairs of giant corrugated cylinders, it is shredded for easy management in the second operation, extraction of the juice by grinding mills.

A series of heavy steel rollers, revolving against each other with tremendous pressure, burst the sugarcane cells and press out the juice. During the final stage of this process sprays of water are used to wet the cane so that the last remaining juice can be recovered. Two products result, sugar juice and cane fibers called *bagasse*. The extracted juice is heated and measured. Then a carefully determined amount of lime is added to neutralize its acidity and to precipitate certain impurities so that they can be removed by settling and filtration. Huge evaporators now take the juice and begin its concentration into sirup, which is boiled in large dome-shaped vacuum pans to the point of crystallization. Liquids boil at lower temperatures under a partial vacuum and the danger of burning the sirup is lessened. The result of this treatment is a mixture of sugar crystals and molasses ready for the centrifugal machines.

A centrifugal machine consists of a round basketlike container with screened sides, contained within a metal shell and mounted on a vertical shaft. The basket spins at a rate of ten to twelve hundred revolutions a minute, throwing off the molasses through the screen and retaining the sugar. At this stage the sugar is known as centrifugal raw sugar. It is a rather sticky mass, reddish brown or somewhat gray in color, which must be refined before it can be used. For this process the sugar, packed in sacks or loaded in bulk, now leaves the vicinity of the cane fields and goes by train and ship to great refineries usually located near the docks. Sometimes it is loaded in bulk directly into the holds of ships and delivered at the refinery wharves by huge conveyors.

At the refinery the first steps are sampling, weighing, laboratory analysis, the payment of customs levies if they are required, and determination of the purchase rate. The raw sugar then goes to a mechanical crusher which breaks up any large lumps that may have formed during shipment. From the crusher it is conveyed to the top of the refinery where it is emptied into a "mingler." Sirup is added at this point and the result is a thick paste called "magma." The magma now flows by gravity into centrifugal machines where it is washed to remove the thin clinging film of molasses that still coats each sugar crystal. The washed crystals go on to the melting tanks to be dissolved in warm water.

Diatomaceous earth—porous and finely divided—is now added to the sugar solution. This type of earth is composed of billions upon billions of exquisitely designed shells of one-celled water plants called diatoms—or sometimes "grass of the sea." Diatomaceous earth will remove many impurities from liquids. After it has been added to the sugar solution the mixture is passed through pressure filters equipped with circular cloth-covered screen discs. All suspended impurities and the earth are removed in this way and the result is a sparkling clear, amber-tinted fluid. To obtain crystal white sugar, the amber color of the sugar solution is removed by means of char filters. These are cylindrical tanks about twenty feet high, containing granulated bone char. The liquid that flows from them is colorless and sparkling. The char, when clogged with impurities, can be cleaned by washing and burning and used over and over. After grading, the liquid passes on to the "pan-house" to be crystallized by steam heating in large dome-shaped vacuum pans. By means of finely adjusted controls an experienced operator can produce the maximum amount of sugar crystals of the required size, and the pans are then emptied into a huge trough-shaped mixer located on the floor below. Revolving paddles in the trough keep the warm mixture of crystals and sirup uniform and prevent it from hardening. Now the sugar crystals must be separated from the sirup by centrifugal machines similar to those used at the beginning of the sugar recovery process.

The centrifugal machines throw off the sirup and deposit the sugar crystals on the screen sides of the containing basket. While the basket is still spinning, sprays of water are played upon the deposit to wash off the last traces of sirup. When the machines are finally stopped the sugar remains in the basket, pure and sparkling white. It is now drawn from the bottom of the centrifugal machines onto conveyors and carried to huge revolving drums where it is dried in a strong current of heated air. The dried granulated sugar crystals are now passed across inclined vibrating screens to be graded according to size. Then on flows the sugar to large storage bins or directly to packaging machines which fill, weigh, and pack it in the convenient sacks and boxes that stock our pantry shelves.

Brown sugars, with their very special cane flavor, are prepared by crystallizing and centrifuging the sugar remaining in the sirup spun off by the centrifugal machines while processing white granulated sugar. Confectioners' sugar is made by grinding pure granulated sugar to a fine powder, and cube sugar is produced by pressing moist granulated sugar into molds on rotating cylinders. The cubes, or tablets, are ejected onto metal plates which are then moved to ovens to be dried and hardened. In another process the sirup for cube sugar goes through the char filters a second time for increased purity and is molded into large blocks, which are sawed and clipped into extra-brilliant tablets.

For the convenience of food manufacturers sugar sirup, or "liquid sugar," also is produced by refineries. The sirup has a sugar content ranging from sixty-six to eighty-eight per cent solid content and is usually made from solutions that have not undergone the final crystallization process. Sugar sirups cut down handling costs and are convenient to use in the bulk preparation of foods. They are shipped in stainless steel tanks or railway tank cars to the manufacturer's plant where they are stored for pumping to any part of the factory as needed.

Sugar is an important heat and energy food, essential to a balanced diet. It is valuable as a preservative and as a flavor improver. Less generally known is the fact that sugar helps the body utilize fat, sparing the proteins for body building and tissue repair. Excessively stringent dieting, which sometimes cuts down dangerously on sugar, can be a menace to health. Actually, in the old days when sugar was both scarce and expensive, doctors often prescribed it as a medicine. English physicians in the mid-nineteenth century used to send weak-chested patients to the West Indies to bask in the January sun and chew the sweet cane. An old account says harvest time on the sugar plantations was a season of rejoicing and that the fresh nourishing juice of the cane brought health and vigor to ailing visitors and to those among the natives who were sickly. Even the oxen, horses, and mules which were given the green tops and skimmings from the boiling house became noticeably sleek and strong at sugar time.

So much for the story of cane sugar, but we have not yet finished our story of these sweet-stemmed grasses. What, in this age of technological progress, can be done with the great heaps of shredded stems left by the crushing machines and the seas of molasses that are produced when sugar is made? Modern science says these two by-products may soon have a commercial usefulness equal to that of the sugar obtained from the cane.

Bagasse was never entirely a waste product in the United States. In spite of certain disadvantages a great deal of it was burned as fuel at the sugar mills. It was also spread in gardens as a mulch and used as poultry litter. Today it is finding much more important uses. Bagasse is being used to make insulating wallboards, plastics, paper, and furfural. Furfural, once a curiosity, is now so important in the oil refining and nylon industries that bagasse has been called upon to supplement oat hulls and corncobs in producing it.

Making paper from bagasse has long been possible but uneconomic from the manufacturer's standpoint. The problems involved have now been solved by research scientists of the United States Department of Agriculture. Under a contract from the department the new technique was tested on a commercial scale by the New York State Department of Forestry at Syracuse. Tests showed that fine bleached papers and newsprint can be made from bagasse pulped by the mechano-chemical method, and also from blends of bagasse and pulpwood. The process is the same as that developed for manufacturing paper from wheat straw and makes use of existing machinery.

As a paper source bagasse is produced in amounts to be reckoned with, more than a pound for every pound of sugar produced. For five and a quarter million tons of cane ground in one year in Louisiana seven hundred and fifty million pounds of raw sugar were produced and more than three billion pounds of bagasse. On a world-wide basis the figures are phenomenal. World sugar production is estimated to be about fifty billion pounds a year and that means that more than fifty billion pounds of bagasse are available for paper and other industrial uses. Already a paper mill in Louisiana is producing from twenty to twenty-five thousand tons a year of bleached papers from whole bagasse and a sugar company is turning out newsprint as a side line.

In addition to cellulose for paper bagasse contains a hard wax, found on the rinds of the canes. During World War II a scarcity of hard wax revived the cane wax industry which had been founded in South Africa in 1916 and abandoned when more economical sources were discovered. Improved methods of extracting the wax are again making cane wax commercially important. It is estimated that about four million pounds a year are potentially available in Louisiana. Sugarcane wax is good for shoe polish, carbon paper, and floors.

And now we come to molasses, that other by-product of sugar production. For every ton of raw sugar there is a half-ton or more of molasses and in Louisiana alone this amounts to about 220,000 tons a year. A small fraction of this tonnage fills the demand for edible sirup. What can be done with all the rest? For one thing it can be mixed with the pith which is sometimes removed from the stalks in paper manufacture to provide a solid, easily handled, high energy food for livestock. Also, 220,000 tons of molasses contain about 114,000 tons of various sugars (there are many kinds) which did not crystallize in the evaporating pans because of their different chemical composition. When fermented, these sugars can produce alcohol, rum, glycerol, lactic and citric acids, and many other products. The list of chemicals that can be derived from the sugars in molasses is almost endless. Among these is aconitic acid. The presence of this acid in cane juice has been known for about three-quarters of a century but there was no large scale use for it until recently when it was found that chemicals derived from it gave transparent plastics superior molding qualities. Aconitic acid (calcium aconitate) is being produced from molasses on a commercial scale in Louisiana. Such research points to the day when every material obtained from sugarcane will find a good use, bringing increased prosperity to those who grow and process it.

As for sugar itself its main industrial use today is in baking and candy-making, meat curing, canning and preserving, ice cream, and soft drinks. But sugar also goes into hair tonics, explosives, photographic supplies, and medicines. It helps tan leather, silver mirrors, make adhesives, cast metals and electroplate them. It is an ingredient of insecticides. It serves as the starting material for the synthesis of vitamin B_2. Mixed with earth it is said to prevent the damping off of conifer seedlings.

L. F. Martin, agricultural research chemist, is not making crystal ball predictions when he surveys the future of sugar. He envisions a carbohydrate age when agricultural products will take the place of coal and petroleum as industrial raw materials. In an article on this subject he says: "More than ten thousand derivatives of sugar . . . have been prepared and described by organic chemists. More than half the derivatives can be obtained directly, or through intermediary steps, from ordinary sugar. Research workers are exploring every possible useful application of the substances and their properties. The first great era of synthetic chemistry was based on the discovery of the almost limitless possibilities of obtaining useful derivatives from coal tar. In more recent times the petroleum age has brought even more products. But coal and petroleum are irreplaceable raw materials. Sugar takes its place with cellulose and starch in the big three of the carbohydrates, which provide a renewable source of raw materials for chemical synthesis, industrial uses, and food. I think it is almost certain that industry will increase its utilization of carbohydrates and that sugar will steadily become more important as we advance in the carbohydrate age."

And with this glimpse into the future we reach the end of our story about the fantastic grass with the rainbow-hued stems, sugarcane—known to ancient civilizations, improved by plant research, and adapted to ever-increasing uses today by the seeming magic of chemistry.

fourteen

Grasses to the Rescue

All things by immortal power
Near or far
Hiddenly
To each other linked are
So thou canst not stir a flower
Without troubling of a star.

Francis Thompson

When man took dominion over the earth he found himself in a world governed by wise and intricate natural laws, whose very existence he did not suspect, and surrounded by a fabulous variety of insect, animal, and plant life whose relation to him and to each other was a complete mystery. Beyond him lay horizons that he could only glimpse—vistas wide as the star patterns in the sky and the awesome void between. But all the progress he could make depended upon his ability to learn the laws that had been put in force when time began and to live in harmony with them.

He was gifted with a very special brain, clever hands with opposable thumbs unlike those of any other creature, and an insatiable curiosity. Thus equipped, he began to explore the earth and the heavens, slowly building the knowledge and understanding that blossomed thousands of years later into the organized and proven knowledge we call science. During his comparatively brief career man has triumphed and blundered, stood momentarily on the heights and momentarily amid chaos. He has learned much, forgotten much, and now he reaches for the stars. But as he seeks the stars he still lacks comprehension of the earth beneath his feet and the debt he owes it.

Over this rock-ribbed world of ours is spread a thin layer of topsoil, deep in some places, altogether wanting in others, averaging about seven inches in depth. Under good conditions of vegetation an inch of it can be built in from three hundred to a thousand years. It is compounded of many ingredients—decayed plants and animals, burrowing insects,

128

minerals from disintegrating rocks, metals, and teeming microscopic life. From place to place it differs in consistency, composition, and color. Upon this thin layer, warmed by the sun, freshened by earth's atmosphere, and watered by the rain, all land plants depend. And man, in his turn, is so dependent upon plants that he would quickly die if deprived of them, starved or suffocated from lack of air.

To understand this fruitful earth, to use wisely the life-giving topsoil and heal its wounds, requires all the knowledge we can command of the intricate functioning of nature.

"All things . . . near or far . . . to each other linked are. . . ."

So delicate is the balance that once the scales are tilted a chain reaction of events begins which can culminate in overwhelming disaster. Forest, grassland, and desert are balanced against each other, plants against water supply and warmth and light from the sun, living creatures against each other and the whole. The flow of rivers, the storage of underground water, even climate, are linked to vegetation, and vegetation to the soil.

Under natural conditions the productive areas of the earth are covered with forests and grasslands, vegetation whose probing roots bind and hold the topsoil and regulate the flow of water and its storage in the earth. Where there is ample moisture forests clothe the steep hillsides and rocky mountain slopes, while the grasses stretch away for miles in the semiarid plains. And so wonderfully have they been adapted to the moisture available that tall, short, and medium grasses are often found growing together, jostling each other for the supply of rainfall. When rainfall is scant, the short grasses predominate; when it is moderate, grasses of medium height take over; when it is wet enough, the tall grasses grow.

If either forest or grassland is destroyed, trouble follows as night the day. The denuded earth, attacked by the wind and the rain, loses some or all of its topsoil. Vegetation deteriorates and the sun-baked land cannot absorb the rain that falls. Gullies and cracks appear, droughts lengthen, streams go dry, and the supply of underground water decreases. Heavy rains, when they come at last, bring destructive floods rather than gentle healing. Rivers, gorged with swollen waters, wash over the surrounding land and sweep the topsoil toward the sea to silt up harbors and reservoirs. On once fertile plains, stripped of their grasses, the wind plays havoc with the dry topsoil, piling it in heaps or burying

it with mineral earth and sand. Thus are created wastelands and creeping deserts where little or nothing can grow.

Overgrazing by cattle in the grassland regions opens the way to
wind erosion and the destruction of pasture lands. Farming grassy
hillsides in our prairie states has brought vast erosion gullies, and plowing up native grasses to establish cultivated crops in regions of insufficient
rainfall has brought disaster to wide areas.

Loss of topsoil, erosion, is a natural process to a certain degree. Since
time began, scientists tell us, soil has been on the move. The rain and
wind, constantly assaulting the earth's surface, move particles of soil
from place to place, gradually changing the contours of the land.
Erosion over eons of time has carved channels for streams, built deltas,
and altered the landscapes of the world. Slowly it seeks to level hill
and mountain, sending them bit by bit to the sea. Every raindrop that
falls upon the bare earth shatters its surface with the impact of a miniature bomb, sending loose particles flying. But where the rain falls on

grassland and forest it is usually absorbed, so that the rate of soil removal is very slow—slow enough to balance the creation of new topsoil from decaying organic matter and weathering rocks.

This delicate and favorable soil balance, established by nature over millions of years, was disturbed by the first men who tilled the earth for food. The forests were cleared, the land breached, and the rate of soil removal was increased. For many centuries the damage went almost unnoticed. When crops became poor in one place, the primitive farmer could move to another and begin again. As population pressures increased and it became necessary to cultivate steep slopes and unstable soils, men began to realize that the rain and wind can waste the earth away.

Looking backward in time with the knowledge we now have, we might easily blame the farmers of an earlier day for impoverishing the more fertile areas of the earth's surface. Or we might say, in the case of our own country, that the government was largely responsible because its early land policy—if indeed it had one—was careless or unwise. To blame either is futile, for censure cannot bring back the squandered heritage. We seek today to correct the errors of the past by hard work, carefully planned. We have the equipment and the knowledge to do it. Have we the steadfast will?

A hundred techniques are used to rebuild worn-out acres and to hold the topsoil. Some of these methods, which seem novel or unusual, were developed by the world's earliest civilizations. The Incas of Peru terraced steep slopes and farmed them. The Egyptians, Chinese, and Babylonians laced arid land with irrigation canals to make it fertile and built dams to contain water for future use.

There is no continent and no land, accessible to man, that has not suffered damage at his hands and the result in many areas has been poverty and famine. Acre by acre the forests have been destroyed that could have guarded the mountain slopes and controlled the streams. Grasslands have been misused so that they can barely support cattle, or have reverted to desert. In our own country the destruction of the basic resources of forest, grassland, topsoil, and water has proceeded more rapidly than in any country of the Old World. The warning voice of the scientist went unheeded as the forests were destroyed and unsuitable grasslands put to the plow. Some thought of the destruction as a war with the wilderness, or as the conquest of nature, but man himself was always under control of the laws he was flouting. For his disharmony the land would ultimately reject him, refusing to yield the crops he needed for food and fiber.

When the forests were stripped from our eastern mountains, the consequence was floods in the cities and towns below as the swollen streams rushed down in the spring, choked with rich forest soil. As the years went by mineral earth followed the topsoil, covering the fertile valley land. Farmers were driven from thousands of rocky New England acres and the forests crept slowly back to cover and restore the land. In the Great Plains area some years later, over millions of acres of ruined grassland, the farmers were rejected again as the dry soil, stripped of cover, became windblown dust. Patiently, during many thousands of years, nature had developed the cover most suitable for these areas—forests for the mountains and hills, and grasses for the plains. The plan had worked well until men intervened. Now we are trying to put the grass and the forests back and to use more wisely the land that is suitable for crops. But the process of restoring the old balance is painful and, in some areas, it may be too late.

In this book we are concerned mainly with the grasses, but their use in the control of erosion is not limited by any means to grassland acres, meadows, playing fields, and lawns. On many acres grass is the only suitable and profitable crop.

When the pioneers, pressing toward the West, crossed the seemingly endless expanse of the Great Plains, they described the region in conflicting terms. Some said it was a rich, lush grassland, for they had come during the years of plentiful rain. Others called it a desert; they had crossed during one of the periods of drought that come regularly to the plains. Then the grasses were brown and sere, their leaves curled to harbor the scant moisture as they awaited rebirth with the next rain.

Settlement of the southern Great Plains by farmers began the year after the blizzard of 1886 had killed many of the cattle on the ranches, and increased until 1892. During this time much of western Kansas, eastern Colorado, and western Texas was converted to farming. By 1892, however, a drought that had begun two years before became severe and the tide of the settlers ebbed toward the East as farm after farm failed. When the rains returned in the late 1890's the settlers flocked back to try farming again. The second good period lasted for about ten years and saw the settlement of the Texas and Oklahoma panhandles, eastern New Mexico, and Colorado. Then, in 1910, another drought began which lasted for three years. It was during this period that the first dust storms came. From 1914 to 1930 rainfall was above average, though there were local droughts and a few bad years. Settlers poured westward again until, by 1931, the land had been plowed on

most of the acreage that was suitable for cultivation and on millions of acres that were not.

In the summer of 1931 another severe drought started. It lasted for seven years in the southern plains and five in the northern. The topsoil began to blow in earnest now, slowly at first, then increasingly, until the air over the Great Plains and far beyond was choked with dust that had been lifted by the wind from millions of barren acres. Finally the winds began to die down, first in the North and two years later in the South. Behind the retreating winds lay millions of acres of seriously damaged land. On some of the land the dunes were piled high as in a desert. On other areas from two to twelve inches of topsoil had been swept away. Farm implements, homes, and barns lay buried in dust. Again the unhappy outward trek began as thousands of farmers abandoned their ruined fields and fled the "dust bowl."

The terrible dust storms of the 1930's left millions of acres of farm and grazing land desolate and bare and brought heartbreak to many. But they had one good result. They focused the attention of the nation on the problem of soil erosion and its possible control. It was soon apparent that, while damage in the dust bowl was highly spectacular, soil erosion just as serious was proceeding elsewhere through the slow, steady removal of topsoil that is known as sheet erosion. One hard rain could remove as much as an inch from a field, lowering its fertility. The nation paused to take stock of its land assets and the facts revealed were appalling. If nothing were done to prevent further destruction, we could look toward a day when the problem of raising enough food to supply a growing population would become as acute as in China and India.

In 1935 Congress passed a soil conservation act, establishing a special service of scientists and technicians for an intensive study of the problem. Part of the legal machinery was the establishment of a national soil bank. Farmers who allowed damaged acres to lie fallow and rest, or planted them in cover crops to stop erosion, were to be compensated by the Federal Government. Meanwhile the scientists, whose warnings had long been unheeded, went eagerly into action. During the early 1940's an extensive survey of the land situation was made by experts of the Soil Conservation Service. This study was carefully refined and published in a special report in 1953.

It was estimated that 35,000,000 acres of soil in the continental United States, that originally had been suitable for crops, had deteriorated to such an extent that it could no longer be farmed successfully. Soil erosion and soil blowing were blamed for the loss of 25,000,000 acres of this total; waterlogging, salting, and the deposit of sediment accounted for the rest. In critical condition were an additional 121,000,-000 acres of cropland, and 138,000,000 more were severely damaged. These could be expected in the future to join the lost acres unless soil-saving practices were applied. Damage on the remaining acres of cropland, 229,000,000 acres, was slight to none. The total acreage suitable for crop production—all these figures added together—was about

478,000,000 acres, of which 69,000,000 were being used only for pasture. The annual rate of loss was about 500,000 acres.

Grazing land not included in farms consisted of 215,000,000 acres of open grassland and shrubs, and about 185,000,000 acres of forest and woodland. Unpastured forest and woodland comprised 286,000,000 acres and 105,000,000 were devoted to special uses—farmsteads, feed-lots, lanes, ditches and roads on farms, and to urban areas, industrial sites, parks, roads, and other rights-of-way. Classified as miscellaneous were 84,000,000 acres, part in farms but mostly consisting of barren land, rock, marshes, deserts, and sand dunes.

As staggering as figures for land losses were, they still did not tell the whole story. They did not include an estimated fifty to one hundred million acres of land, never suited to cultivation, but inadvisedly used for farming in the past. These lands are now deteriorated and abandoned. Nor did they include areas of cropland lost to agriculture through causes other than erosion—the spread of cities and suburbs, industrial expansion, and deliberate inundation for the construction of dams.

The Soil Conservation Service, still comparatively new, has gone about its work quietly and tactfully since most of the productive land in the United States is privately owned. Success depends upon the good will of farmers and ranchers and their cooperative action. The earliest work of the service was necessarily educational. Staff scientists and technicians worked with interested individuals on conservation problems of both soil and water. Later the emphasis was broadened to encompass small watershed areas where runoff and flooding were acute, and other areas where special problems existed. The loss of land to cultivation was held to half a million acres a year and special care was being taken to prevent further deterioration on land in serious or critical condition. In the future the losses are expected to show a downward trend.

Meanwhile, as conservation farming goes into practice, the rolling American countryside is taking on a new look—a pattern of stripes and ribbony curves in tones of brown and green. A variety of methods is employed to stabilize topsoil. Most of the commonly used techniques involve grasses—the key to soil conservation. Grasses not only prevent erosion but are the most efficient of all plant soil builders. Their roots may penetrate the earth to a depth of four or five feet in a dense tangle that keeps even sand stable. The roots and stems of the grasses, when they die, enrich the soil of exhausted acres, especially if they are grown with nitrogen-fixing legumes—clovers, lespedezas, alfalfa, and other such plants. While doing its soil-saving work grass can be nibbled by cattle and still flourish, because its growing area is buried deep in the plant from where it pushes ever upward. Nongrass plants are generally destroyed when they are topped.

In conservation farming a large part of every farm is kept in meadow on either a permanent or rotation basis. Grasses, in rotation planting, contribute valuable organic material to the soil when they are plowed under with their accompanying legumes. Used this way, they are called "green manure."

On western ranches grass is a crop. On a well-kept range it grows each season from two to three hundred pounds of forage an acre, or two to three million pounds on a ranch of ten thousand acres. That is enough to produce seventy-five to a hundred thousand pounds of meat for the nation's tables.

Cattle, sheep, and other farm animals are not alone in their dependence upon grass. Nearly all animals depend upon it either directly, through grazing, or indirectly through their reliance for sustenance on grass-eating animals. In addition, countless microscopic creatures in the soil live on the roots of grasses. As root and organism decay they improve the soil, and thus the grasses, more than any other family of plants, efficiently condition the soil for continued high production. We have in the United States about a billion acres of grassland. Where it is in luxuriant condition it can be kept that way through proper care. Where the grass cover has been lost through erosion or overgrazing, it can often be restored. Allowed to do its work without interference, grass can reclaim many of the eroded acres of the plains. With a little help from men it can clothe and heal many more.

On eroded and eroding cropland, grass, properly used, will stop the drift of the topsoil and improve the land. It will hold the slopes of watersheds, guarding the water supply of cities and towns and protecting them against floods. Wherever the land is not held by forests the grasses seek to cover and protect it. Thus taking a tip from nature, the modern farmer makes new use of the grasses and becomes absorbed in their infinite variety.

The present interest in grasses can be traced to the men of the Soil Conservation Service, who in a brief span of years have introduced a new agricultural concept. Working through locally organized, farmer managed, soil conservation districts—subdivisions of state governments —these scientists and technicians are at the service of land owners everywhere. By January, 1958, farmers and ranchers had organized conservation districts covering well over a billion and a half acres in the United States and its territories. This brought about 93 per cent of all farms and ranches in the United States within the boundaries of a district organized for soil conservation. Farmers in these areas can obtain technical advice in planning the best use of their land by applying to local district headquarters of the Soil Conservation Service.

Farmers and ranchers have been alert to take advantage of the expert help offered. As of January, 1958, one and three-quarter millions had signed agreements with soil conservation districts and were developing and applying conservation measures on more than half a billion acres of land.

The concept underlying the program, which includes soil, water, forest, grassland, and wildlife, is to keep the earth covered with vegetation so that the topsoil cannot be washed or blown away. Some of the measures recommended can be outlined as follows:

If row crops that require cultivation are to be grown, plant them alternately with grass crops—in strips—using techniques that discourage runoff and hold the water on the land.

Techniques that discourage runoff, with its burden of topsoil and menace of gully and flood, are based on the primitive knowledge that water runs downhill, seeking its own level. Except on perfectly flat land, therefore, forget the nicety of the straight furrow and plow with the contour of the land in sweeping curves, even on gentle slopes. Then, instead of forming a runway for water, each line cut by the plow will throw the earth back in a horizontal ridge that will serve as a miniature dam.

And even with strip planting, whether straight or on the contour, keep the fields as level as possible. If necessary use terraces, taking care that the outlet ends discharge surplus water into grassed waterways so a gully is not started. Where slope meets slope to form a gentle depression in which water tends to collect during rains, consider establishing such a waterway to slow the tide and absorb it, and cut the grass in the waterway for hay. If, through imperfect farming practice in the past, the land has begun to gully, do not wait until great fissures appear or branching side gullies. Get the land under control as rapidly as possible. If it is too steep for grasses to manage the job, plant trees. Mechanical barriers will not stop a gully. On land not suitable for growing crops because of soil deterioration or other reasons, consider a permanent meadow. On rocky slopes unsuitable for either cropland or meadow, let the trees come back or plant them yourself. Farm woodlots are a paying proposition.

And what of our natural grasslands, the great rolling green seas of the plains? Ought they, as some suggested during the drought of the 1930's, be given over entirely to grass? Certainly not. We need the land for crops, and a carefully prepared soil survey of the Great Plains shows that three-quarters of the land under cultivation is entirely suitable for continuous farming. However, special techniques should be followed.

Most of the soil blowing that brings desert conditions to dry areas of the plains begins on poor land that should have been left in grass, but sometimes it starts on good land improperly farmed or on severely over-grazed range land. When wind erosion begins on such land it is likely to spread. Particles of soil, carried across the boundaries of fields and farms, blast loose other particles when they strike bare ground and these augment the cutting blast that finally shears off growing plants at the base or covers them with drifts of loose soil. The drifts are then ready to blow, if the wind returns, to build dunes, or to cover a wide area. How can the drifting soil be held and good agricultural methods be practiced in such a region, subject as it is and has always been to recurring droughts?

The long-range plan must vary from one area of the plains to the next so that each acre is used according to its capability, under practices that not only protect but improve it. The 14,000,000 unsuitable acres now being farmed, experts say, should be converted to grassland as rapidly as possible. The planting can be done at little cost during a period of rainfall. This procedure will return to profitable use land that is not good for farming because it is too sandy, the topsoil too thin, or moisture insufficient. To compensate for the withdrawal of this land from agricultural use, other grassland areas classified as suitable for cultivation can be plowed. On all land used for crops in the plains, conservation practices should be followed which have been found effective in preventing erosion when the rains fail. In other words, every year should be regarded as a potential year of drought.

The construction of terraces on sloping land, contour plowing, the use of winter cover crops, and stubble mulching all help to conserve water and reduce wind erosion on cultivated land of the Great Plains. Stubble mulching is a year round practice which leaves as much of the crop residues as possible on the surface of the soil until the next crop is planted. Stalks cut high at harvest time, leaves and stems left on the surface instead of being plowed under or burned, protect the land from wind and rainfall. Plowing is done with long sweeps which pass under the surface instead of turning or stirring the soil. The old roots also protect the productive topsoil from wind and dashing rains. The new crop often is seeded in the old stubble so that the soil has some protection until the new vegetation comes up to take over the task. Strips of sorghums and other wind-resistant crops are recommended for alternate planting with tilled crops on large fields likely to blow. These are grown also in rotation with wheat and cotton. Winter cover crops are needed on cotton fields subject to erosion.

On range land, especially during periods of drought, grazing should be adjusted carefully to the amount of forage grass to avoid damage. On much range land that is now on the downgrade through misuse, brush control and reseeding is necessary, but sometimes all that is needed to bring back a healthy stand of grass is a judiciously placed fence. A good reserve supply of hay or silage tides over the periods of drought on a well-run ranch when overgrazing could damage the range.

Once a drought is under way and the soil blowing, neither rain nor snow is likely to stay the damage on unprotected land. Long range schemes must be pigeonholed temporarily and emergency measures taken. On fields where plowing will bring clods of heavy moist soil to the surface, emergency tillage—done properly and at the right time—may check wind erosion. As soon as the field starts to blow, strips of land are tilled—straight or on the contour depending on the lay of the land —across the path of the prevailing winds. If, after a time of blowing and resting, the winds rise again, the spaces between the tilled strips are plowed. But plowing strips to trip the winds is strictly an emergency

method. As soon as there is enough moisture in the ground to start plants growing a cover crop should be seeded, and during such a time every weed that sprouts should be regarded as a soil saving ally. The plants seeded for cover are wind-resistant grasses such as the sorghums, Sudan grass, broomcorn, and millet. Or, if rainfall is adequate, the crop can be a grain—wheat, rye, or barley.

Early in the 1950's drought returned to the treeless sweep of the Great Plains and again on millions of acres the topsoil began to blow. But many farmers and ranchers had been practicing good conservation methods since the disastrous dust storms of the 1930's. On the whole they fared better than those who were still traveling the old careless route, but some of them saw their lands and crops damaged by blowing dust from the unprotected fields of their neighbors. In areas where conservation farming predominated, where eroded cropland had been converted to grass, where stubble mulching was generally practiced and cover crops grown, the drought brought little severe damage. Without the farmers who practiced conservation the damage would have been much more extensive than it was—but there were still not enough of them. United action on a community or regional basis is needed to bring the full benefits of conservation practices.

Soil-saving techniques, whether applied on the plains, watersheds, hills, mountains, or cropland, do not embody merely an idealist's dream of preserving our natural resources for generations yet unborn. They form a practical plan that can enable us to maintain and improve those resources while making full use of them—a plan that is economically profitable. A farmer in Wisconsin started a conservation program in 1939 which included a blueprint for every acre of his land. He sought and received expert advice from scientists and technicians, through his district conservation unit, and made use of all the soil and water saving techniques that were recommended. His farm yield began to increase almost immediately. Within a period of ten years he was harvesting ninety bushels of corn an acre on land that had yielded fifty-one. Around him neighboring farmers managed to boost their corn crop from forty-two to forty-nine bushels an acre. The crop increase of the farmer practicing conservation was five times that of the county average.

In Waco, Texas, during three drought years, on a conservation-farmed watershed, the corn harvest was greater by almost half than on a farm managed in the old way. Cotton yields were two-thirds higher. On poor range land, stripped of brush and reseeded to grass, beef production doubled and quadrupled as the grasses responded to proper care. For better seed, fertilizers, and improved growing methods alone cannot bring a farm to its greatest production. The basis must always be the proper use and management of the soil. Today, through the nation's many soil conservation districts, information needed on use and management of the land is available to every farmer and rancher. Experts will help make a wise plan for the use of the land and often see that there is help in financing the change-over to new and better practice. And through the willing cooperation a democracy encourages we shall yet have green acres where creeping deserts threaten.

When farmers and ranchers adapt their land to its best use and strive to maintain, or restore, a favorable balance of soil, water, and plant life, they are working within the scope of omnipotent natural laws. Nature, ruthless in punishment when abused, responds graciously to cooperative overtures. The land thrills to new life as the grass heals its wounds, and crops increase. Forests return to their old locations and the streams run pure once more. Droughts lessen and floods decrease. Where poverty bred of worn-out acres threatened, prosperity comes again.

The grasses, so unassuming yet so important, can accomplish miracles if we let them work. Should they fail for a single season, famine would put an end to life on earth. For science has proved what wise Isaiah knew instinctively some twenty-seven centuries ago:

"All flesh is grass, and the goodliness thereof is as the flower of the field."

Some Books
for Further Reading

Beard, Miriam, *History of the Business Man,* New York, The Macmillan Company, 1938.

Blanchan, Neltje, *The New Nature Library,* Vol. 8, New York, Doubleday, Page and Company, 1914.

Deerr, Noel, *Cane Sugar,* London, Norman Rodger, 1911.

Dickson, James G., *Diseases of Field Crops,* Second edition, New York, McGraw-Hill Book Company, 1956.

Fairchild, David, *Exploring for Plants,* New York, The Macmillan Company, 1930.

Hartwig, G. L., *The Tropical World,* London, Longmans, Green, and Company, 1863.

Hitchcock, A. S., *A Text-Book of Grasses,* New York, The Macmillan Company, 1914.

Schenk, Gustav, *The Book of Poisons,* New York, Rinehart and Company, 1955.

Sears, Paul B., *Deserts on the March,* Norman, Oklahoma, University of Oklahoma Press, 1954.

Southworth, John Van Duyn, *The Story of the World,* New York, Pocket Books, 1954.

Travels of Marco Polo, edited by Manuel Komroff, Garden City, New York, Garden City Publishing Company, 1941.

Tsui Chi, *A Short History of Chinese Civilization,* New York, G. P. Putnam's Sons, 1943.

Universal History, Vol. 1., edited by J. A. Hammerton, New York, Wise and Company, 1937.

Weatherwax, Paul, *Indian Corn in Old America,* New York, The Macmillan Company, 1954.

Yearbooks of Agriculture, 1948, 1950–1951, 1952, 1957, Washington, D.C., United States Department of Agriculture.

Index